MAP PROJECTIONS

METHUEN'S ADVANCED GEOGRAPHIES

MAP PROJECTIONS

by

GEORGE P. KELLAWAY,

B.Sc., F.R.G.S.

LECTURER AT ST. JOHN'S COLLEGE, YORK

WITH 75 DIAGRAMS

METHUEN & CO. LTD. LONDON
36 Essex Street, Strand, W.C.2

First published in 1946

BOOK
PRODUCTION
WAR ECONOMY
STANDARD

THIS BOOK IS PRODUCED IN
COMPLETE CONFORMITY WITH THE
AUTHORIZED ECONOMY STANDARDS

PRINTED IN GREAT BRITAIN

PREFACE

THE chief aim of this book is to provide students, more especially students of geography, with a logical treatment of the commoner map projections; but, in view of the ever-growing importance of maps in the modern world, and the need for their careful interpretation, it is hoped that the work may also be of value to a wider public than that for which it was originally planned.

The student of geography seldom has an opportunity to carry his study of mathematics to the 'advanced' stage, a limitation which has constantly been borne in mind by the writer. Yet some knowledge of mathematics is indispensable if the study of map projections is to be more than merely superficial; but, provided the student has a good working knowledge of the basic principles of elementary plane trigonometry, he should experience no very great difficulties. The appendices contain useful formulae for the guidance of those who have little mathematical background.

To meet the varied needs of the many different types of student, each projection has been discussed separately, and the work has been divided into parts, but the essential unity of the subject has been recognized throughout. The syllabuses, in so far as they relate to map projections, of the 'intermediate' examinations (Intermediate Degree, Higher School Certificate, Advanced Courses in Training Colleges, etc.) are adequately covered by Parts I and III, while the whole book should prove sufficient for the obligatory papers in Map Work for the University Degree. The work is not intended, however, for those students whose study of map projections is of a highly specialized nature.

The writer has endeavoured to achieve logical reality by relating the various projections to their basic mathematical principles; and, throughout, the projections have been developed from a globe, or 'reduced' earth, which might be described as the 'generating' globe. It is important that the student should think of a projection as an attempt to represent the globe, or some part of it, on a flat surface. Further, the student is urged to construct the projections when studying them, for practice in the drawing assists the understanding. Unfortunately for the student, many of the projections when drawn on a small scale, especially some of the conicals, look very much alike, and it is almost impossible to distinguish between them when only small areas are mapped. It may be desirable, therefore, to construct the projection for a much larger area than that for which it would normally be used; in this way the tendency of the errors becomes more readily apparent. In this book, for example, all the conical projections have been developed for a complete hemisphere, a far larger area than that for which they can reasonably be employed; yet to represent the 'ideal' area, on the scale which is possible in a book such as this, would be pointless. When constructing his own projections, however, the student should always attempt to assess the extent of the area appropriate to each projection.

I have to thank the following examining bodies for permission to reproduce selected questions: University of Cambridge, University of London, Joint Matriculation Board, Oxford and Cambridge Schools Examination Board.

G. P. KELLAWAY

1946

CONTENTS

PART I

PART II

PART III

PART I

CHAPTER I

THE GLOBE AND THE MAP

THE true shape of the earth approximates to a sphere, and the only true map is, therefore, a 'reduced' earth, or globe, which has been modelled on the earth; when the earth is represented, either in part or as a whole, on a flat surface, certain obvious difficulties inevitably arise.

A *very small* part of the earth's surface, that is, its true water-surface, is sensibly flat, and, for most practical purposes, no serious error is introduced into map-making if it is regarded as actually so. The larger the area surveyed, however, the more difficult is the problem of representing it, with any pretence to accuracy, on a flat map; it is this problem which is the essence of map projection.

The position of any point on the earth's surface can be accurately and fully defined by reference to a parallel of latitude *and* a meridian of longitude; for example, $y°$ N. or S. of the equator, and $x°$ E. or W. of the Meridian of Greenwich. The problem of representing the earth's surface on a flat map can therefore be resolved into the most convenient method of plotting selected parallels and meridians.

Much will depend upon the precise purpose for which the map is required, but, in any case, the map will be no more than a compromise, and the limitations of all maps must be appreciated from the outset.

Parallels of Latitude. A brief examination of the globe will suffice to emphasize the more important characteristics of parallels of latitude.

Each parallel is clearly a circle, running round the globe, and maintaining uniform distance from the poles. The *central* parallel is the equator, which lies equidistant from the two poles. Each parallel lies wholly in its own plane, which is at right angles to the axis of the earth.

The parallels are not all of equal length; they range from a point at each of the poles to the circumference of the globe at the equator.

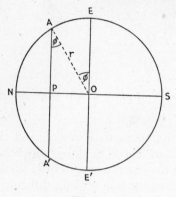

FIG. I

Radius of parallel in latitude
$\phi = EP = r.\cos\phi$

The latitude of any particular parallel may be defined as the angle subtended at the centre of the globe by a north-south arc of surface, which is bounded by the equator and the particular parallel in question. In *Fig. 1*, which represents a section through the centre of the globe, the axis (*N-S*) is shown in the plane of the section. The plane of the equator is at right angles to *NS*; *E* and *E'* are therefore opposite points on the equator. The radius of the equator is given by *EO*, which is equal to the radius of the globe (r). The length of the equator is therefore $2\pi r$, the circumference of the globe. The arc *AE* runs north-south, and it subtends an angle ϕ at *O*, the centre of the globe; when *A* is in the northern hemisphere the point *A* is therefore in latitude $\phi°$N. Since the plane of the parallel through *A* is parallel to the plane of the equator, *AA'* is drawn parallel to *EE'*; so *A* and *A'* are opposite points on the parallel of latitude $\phi°$N. The radius of this parallel is given by *AP*, which is $r.\cos\phi$, and the length of the parallel is therefore $2\pi r.\cos\phi$. Thus, the lengths of the parallels of latitude vary directly as the cosine of the latitude.

Taking the length of the equator as the unit, the lengths of selected parallels are as follow:

Equator	1
Latitude 15°	0·96593
Latitude 30°	0·86603
Latitude 45°	0·70711
Latitude 60°	0·50000
Latitude 75°	0·25882
Poles	0

Meridians of Longitude. The meridians are semicircles, running north-south from one pole to the other; two opposite meridians, however, make a complete circle. In *Fig. 1* the two semicircles, *NAES* and *NA'E'S*, are opposite meridians; together they make a circle, which is the circumference of the globe.

There is no obvious *central* meridian, but an arbitrary choice has been made, namely, the *Meridian of Greenwich* (the *Prime Meridian*).

Each meridian lies wholly in its own plane, but the planes of the different meridians all intersect along the axis of the globe, just as the 'planes' of separation between the sections of an orange all intersect along the 'axis' of the orange. The longitude of any particular meridian may therefore be defined as the angle between the plane which contains the Prime Meridian and the plane which contains the particular meridian in question, due regard being paid to the direction *east* or *west*.

The meridians are all of equal length. They are widest apart at the equator, and they converge towards the poles. Further, every meridian intersects every parallel at right angles.

The spacing of the parallels along the meridians is at once evident from *Fig. 1*. The arc distance AE is equal to $r.\phi^c$, where r is the radius of the globe, and ϕ^c the angle of latitude expressed in circular measure (radians). The spacing of the parallels on a globe of unit radius is given in the following table:

				North-south arc distance measured from the equator
To Latitude 15°	.	.	.	0·2618
Latitude 30°	.	.	.	0·5236
Latitude 45°	.	.	.	0·7854
Latitude 60°	.	.	.	1·0472
Latitude 75°	.	.	.	1·3090
Latitude 90°	.	.	.	1·5708

It is evident that the spacing of the parallels along the meridians is perfectly uniform. There is, for example, exactly the same arc distance between the equator and the parallel 15°N. as there is between the North Pole and the parallel 75°N. This statement assumes a true earth-sphere, of course, and therefore needs some qualification. The precise shape of the earth is usually referred to as a 'geoid', a term which conveys nothing beyond *earth-shaped*. The 'reduced' earth, on the scale with which we are accustomed to deal, however, differs so little from the perfect sphere, that any deviation from the true sphere is not apparent when the projections are drawn. To regard the earth as anything other than a sphere is to introduce refinements which cannot be realized in practice, for the variations which might reasonably be expected to occur in the material on which the maps are drawn, due to changes in atmospheric conditions, are invariably of a higher order than the theoretical refinements.

The meridians are spaced uniformly along each parallel of latitude, but the actual arc distance between any two given meridians varies from latitude to latitude. In *Fig. 1*, the length of the parallel in latitude $\phi°$ is $2\pi r.\cos\phi$; hence, by giving the appropriate value to ϕ, the spacing of the meridians in any latitude can be determined. Thus, considering meridians at intervals of 15°, both east and west of Greenwich, the arc distance between any one and the next will be $\frac{15}{360}$ of the total length of the parallel in that latitude. But the total length of the parallel varies directly as the cosine of the latitude; hence the spacing between meridians also varies directly as the cosine of the latitude.

Summary. The salient properties, in relation to map projection, of parallels and meridians on the globe may be summarized thus:

(i) Parallels of latitude are circles, which are parallel to the equator. The length of the parallel in any given latitude varies directly as the cosine of the latitude. The parallels are uniformly spaced along the meridians.

(ii) Meridians of longitude are semicircles, which are all of equal length, namely, half that of the equator. They are spaced at uniform angular intervals; the arc distance between the meridians, in any given latitude, varies directly as the cosine of the latitude.

(iii) Every meridian intersects every parallel at right angles.

The Flat Map. When drawing a network, or graticule, of parallels and meridians on a flat surface, it is impossible to preserve all the properties summarized above; distortion, in some form or other, is inevitable.

Broadly speaking, the most important factors to be considered in the preparation of a map are: (*a*) the *position* of the region in relation to the earth's surface as a whole; (*b*) the *direction* which any one point in the region bears to another; (*c*) the *distance* between any given points in the region; (*d*) the *shape* of the region; (*e*) the accurate representation of the *area* of the region; and (*f*) the ease and accuracy with which the map can be constructed.

Since any flat map must, of necessity, be only a compromise, the main problem is to select the predominating property essential to each particular case, and to preserve that property as faithfully as possible; or, if several properties are to be shown in combination, a careful balance must be achieved to preserve accuracy where it is most essential. That is the essence of map projection.

A map projection is simply a device for representing the parallels and meridians of the earth's surface on a flat map. When *small* areas are being mapped, it is possible to obtain sensibly accurate representation of all properties, but in the case of *large* areas, something must be sacrificed. The problem is thus really a matter of selecting the projection which best satisfies the specific requirements in each particular case.

The advantages and limitations of the various projections will become clear as the different types, and the principles which underlie them, are studied.

CLASSIFICATION OF PROJECTIONS

The many and varied map projections in common use can generally be classified according to the principles which underlie their mode of development, but, before attempting a classification, it will be instructive for the reader to examine the basic considerations involved.

Throughout the present book the projections are all developed from a globe, or 'reduced' earth, which may therefore be conveniently regarded as the 'generating' globe; in this way the properties and limitations of each projection, and the differences between the various projections, become readily apparent. Students who find difficulty in visualizing problems 'in the solid' are advised to make appropriate models, which they will find most helpful when 'transforming' the three-dimensional earth-sphere into the two-dimensional map projection.

Perspective Projections. A first group in a general classification might well be the strictly geometrical projections, namely, those derived from the 'generating' globe by processes which are, in fact, 'projection' as it is popularly understood. These are known as *perspective*, or *geometrical*, projections. Variety within the group is obtained by varying the position of the point of origin of the projection, and by varying the nature of the surface on which the projection is to be made.

POINT OF ORIGIN. Although the point of origin, or 'view point', of the projection may be chosen to suit any particular requirement, three positions are commonly used, namely, (i) the centre of the globe, (ii) a point on the surface of the globe, remote from the surface of projection, and (iii) a point at an infinite distance.

SURFACE OF PROJECTION. The surface on which the projection is to be made is likewise chosen to suit individual requirements. Three types are in general use, namely, (i) a *plane*, which is usually, but not invariably, tangential to the globe at some specified point; (ii) a *cylinder*, which either envelops, or intersects, the globe in some specified manner; and (iii) a *cone*, which either rests upon, or intersects, the globe in some specified manner. (The plane and the cylinder may both be regarded as special cases of the cone, for they are, in a sense, the extreme limiting forms of the cone. When the apical angle of the cone becomes zero, the cone becomes a cylinder; at the other extreme, the cone becomes a plane.) After projection, these surfaces are 'opened out flat'; the cylinder, by cutting along a line parallel to the axis, and the cone, by cutting along a line running from the base to the apex. Thus can the three-dimensional earth-sphere be 'transformed' into the two-dimensional map projection.

Non-Perspective Projections. An appropriate second group embraces projections which are, in effect, derived from their perspective counterparts by suitable modification. They are not, therefore, 'projected' in the usual sense of the term, and are consequently known as *non-perspective* projections. The method and degree of modification can be adjusted to suit any particular requirement, and, because they can be so readily adapted to individual circumstances, the non-perspective group assumes great importance. Thus, it is possible to ensure that *areas* are strictly comparable over the entire projection, whether the projection be *conical* (projected on to a cone), *cylindrical* (projected on to a cylinder), or *zenithal* (projected on to a plane); such a projection is said to be an *equal-area projection*. Or, it is possible to ensure that the *scale* at any point over the entire projection shall be the *same in all directions*, although the actual scale must necessarily vary from one part of the projection to another; such a projection preserves the *shape of small areas*, and is said to be *orthomorphic*. Yet again, it is possible to preserve other properties of the *scale*; for example, the meridian scale may be everywhere correct. Thus, by singling out some particular property of the globe for special consideration, it is possible, by suitable adaptation, to preserve that property on the projection.

Conventional Projections. A third group includes those projections which are purely conventional in form, and in which the idea of 'projection', as generally understood, is not apparent. Instead, the parallels and meridians are drawn so as to conform to some arbitrarily chosen principle. Included in this group are some very valuable projections, especially those designed to show the whole world on one map.

CHAPTER II

ZENITHAL (AZIMUTHAL) PROJECTIONS POLAR CASES

PERSPECTIVE

IN this class of projection the parallels and meridians of the 'generating' globe are projected geometrically from a point on to a plane, which is tangential to the globe, and at right angles to the line joining the point of origin to the point of contact (*see Figs 2, 4, and 5*).

Several distinctive map projections result, according to the position of the point of origin of the projection; but they have one property in common, namely, that *direction, or bearing, from the centre of the map is true*; they are therefore often referred to as '*azimuthal*' projections.

THE GNOMONIC PROJECTION

The point of origin (or 'view point') of the projection is the centre of the 'generating' globe. The plane is tangential in any desired position. When the plane is tangential at either of the two poles, the resulting projection is referred to as the *polar* case; when the plane is tangential at some point on the equator, as the *equatorial* case; when the plane is tangential elsewhere, as the *oblique* case.

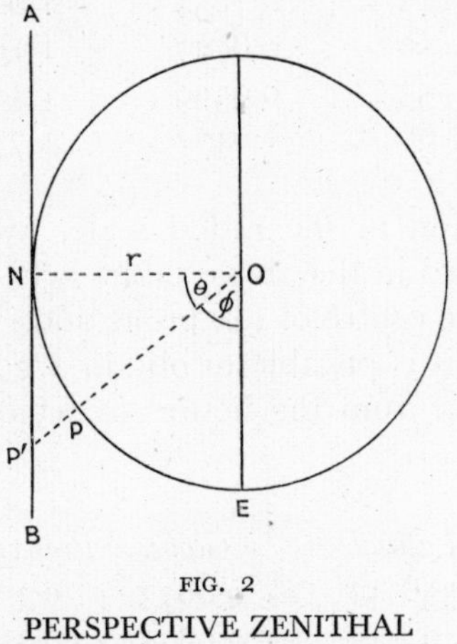

Fig. 2 represents a section through the centre of the globe, at right angles to the plane of projection (*AB*), which is tangential to the globe at the North Pole (*N*). Let *P* be a point on the surface of the globe, and let the 'ray' *OP* be produced to cut the tangent-plane at *P'*. Then *P'* is the geometrical projection of *P*,

FIG. 2

PERSPECTIVE ZENITHAL PROJECTION (GNOMONIC)

The projection is made from the centre of the globe on to a plane which is tangential to the 'generating' globe.

7

from the origin O, on to the plane AB; P' is, in fact, the *gnomonic* projection of P.

Let the radius of the globe be r, and let the point P be in latitude ϕ; that is, $\angle EOP=\phi°$. Let $\angle PON=\theta°$; then $\theta=(90-\phi)$.

Hence $NP'=r.\tan\theta=r.\cot\phi$.

But　　$NP=r.\theta^c$, where θ^c is in circular measure (radians).

Thus if θ is very small, that is, if P is very near the pole, $\tan\theta=\theta^c$ (very nearly), and the distance of P' from N is very nearly equal to the distance of P from N.

Over a very small area near the centre of the projection, therefore, *distances measured from the centre* are very nearly true; that is, they are very nearly equal to corresponding distances on the 'generating' globe.

When θ increases, that is, when P moves farther from the pole, $\tan\theta$ becomes progressively greater than θ^c, and distances measured from the centre of the projection are therefore exaggerated, to an ever-increasing extent. In such a case it would be necessary to know the *radial scale* of the map at each parallel of latitude, for it would increase with increasing distance from the centre, as the following table shows:

$\theta°$	θ^c	$\tan\theta$	$\theta°$	θ^c	$\tan\theta$
5	0·0873	0·0875	35	0·6109	0·7002
10	0·1745	0·1763	40	0·6981	0·8391
15	0·2618	0·2679	45	0·7854	1·0000
20	0·3491	0·3640	50	0·8727	1·1918
25	0·4363	0·4663	55	0·9599	1·4281
30	0·5236	0·5774	60	1·0472	1·7321

Actually, the glaring exaggeration in the radial scale, away from the centre, is somewhat masked in the above table, because all distances are measured from the centre of the projection. By a process of subtraction, however, it is possible to obtain a good indication of the radial scale, even from the figures as set out, thus:

Latitude	Globe	Projection	Latitude	Globe	Projection
5°–10°	0·0873	0·0888	35°–40°	0·0873	0·1389
10°–15°	0·0873	0·0916	40°–45°	0·0873	0·1609
15°–20°	0·0873	0·0961	45°–50°	0·0873	0·1918
20°–25°	0·0873	0·1023	50°–55°	0·0873	0·2363
25°–30°	0·0873	0·1111	55°–60°	0·0873	0·3040

It is now very evident that the exaggeration in the radial scale becomes increasingly pronounced away from the centre.

In the *polar* case of the *gnomonic*, the parallels of latitude are projected as circles, described about the pole as centre.· The meridians of longitude are projected as radii, uniformly spaced at their correct angular intervals.

On the globe the length of the parallel in latitude ϕ is $2\pi r.\cos \phi$; on the projection the length of this same parallel is $2\pi r.\cot \phi$. The following table shows the relation between $\cos \phi$ and $\cot \phi$ for selected values of ϕ, and hence gives an indication of the scale along the parallels, both on the globe and on the projection:

$\phi°$	$\cos \phi$	$\cot \phi$	$\phi°$	$\cos \phi$	$\cot \phi$
85	0·0872	0·0875	55	0·5736	0·7002
80	0·1736	0·1763	50	0·6428	0·8391
75	0·2588	0·2679	45	0·7071	1·0000
70	0·3420	0·3640	40	0·7660	1·1918
65	0·4226	0·4663	35	0·8192	1·4281
60	0·5000	0·5774	30	0·8660	1·7321

Quite clearly, the *scale along the parallels* also increases away from the centre of the projection, but at a rate which is different from that along the meridians. Thus, in latitude 30° ($\phi=30°$; $\theta=60°$), the scale along the projected parallels is twice the scale of the globe; but the scale along the meridians in latitude 30° is four times the scale of the globe.

This difficulty with the scale, away from the centre of the projection, applies equally to all cases of the *gnomonic*, but it is only in the *polar* case that the meridians are radii, and that the parallels are concentric circles. In the *equatorial* and *oblique* cases it is accordingly more difficult to determine the scales along the meridians and parallels.

All cases of the *gnomonic* possess one important property which is shared by no other projection; since the projection is made geometrically from the centre of the globe on to a plane which is tangential to the globe, all *great circles are projected as straight lines*. The shortest *arc distance* between two points on the surface of a sphere is the smaller part of the great circle which passes through the points; hence the shortest distance between two points on the surface of the globe is shown on the *gnomonic* by straight lines. Important as great circles are in navigation, however, the *gnomonic* is not generally suitable for *direction*, which is the essence

of navigation, and it is therefore used only in special circumstances. A projection which shows *constant bearing* by straight lines
is preferable for navigation (see p. 38).

Summary of Properties. For a *small* area near the centre of the
projection, the representation is not unsatisfactory, and the
advantages may be summarized thus: (i) the relative positions
of places can be accurately and clearly shown; (ii) direction from
the centre is always true (in the *polar* case, either due north or

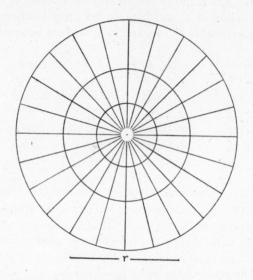

FIG. 3

POLAR GNOMONIC (developed from a globe of radius *r*)

The meridians are drawn, radiating from the pole, at intervals of 15°; the
parallels are drawn, as concentric circles about the pole as centre, also at
intervals of 15°.

due south, according to which pole is selected as the centre;
(iii) distances are reasonably accurate in all directions; (iv) great
circles are projected as straight lines; and (v) the projection is
easily constructed.

Limitations. (i) Away from the centre of the projection, distances
rapidly become increasingly exaggerated; in the *polar* case, more
so along the meridians than along the parallels; (ii) the shape of
regions, except in the case of those very near the centre, is distorted, and the amount of distortion increases away from the
centre; (iii) the area of regions, except in the case of those very
near the centre, is exaggerated, and the exaggeration increases

rapidly away from the centre; (iv) direction, other than that from the centre, is not always readily apparent; and (v) from the method of projection it will be at once clear that a complete hemisphere cannot be projected on one map.

Construction. With centre N, the projection of the North Pole, describe circles of radii $r.\cot \phi$, where ϕ is any required angle of latitude. These circles are the projected parallels of latitude. The meridians can now be drawn, as straight lines, radiating from N at their true angular intervals.

Fig. 3 shows the development of the *polar gnomonic*; the *equatorial* and *oblique* cases are discussed on p. 73 *et seq.*

THE STEREOGRAPHIC (ORTHOMORPHIC) PROJECTION

The point of origin of the projection is on the surface of the 'generating' globe, diametrically opposite the point of contact of the plane of projection, which is tangential to the globe in

any desired position; so *polar*, *equatorial*, and *oblique* cases are all possible.

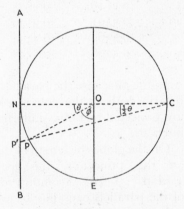

Fig. 4 represents a section through the centre of the globe, at right angles to the plane of projection (AB), which is tangential to the globe at the North Pole (N); the point of origin (C) is also in the plane of the section. Let P be a point on the surface of the globe, and let the 'ray' CP be produced to cut the plane of projection at P'. Then P' is the geometrical projection of P, from the origin C, on to the plane AB; P' is, in fact, the *stereographic* projection of P.

FIG. 4

PERSPECTIVE ZENITHAL PROJECTION (STEREOGRAPHIC)

The projection is made from the end of the diameter which is opposite the point of contact of the plane of projection.

Let the radius of the globe be r, and let the point P be in latitude ϕ; that is, $\angle EOP = \phi°$. Let $\angle PON = \theta$; then $\theta = (90 - \phi)$, and $\angle PCN = \frac{1}{2}\theta = (45 - \frac{1}{2}\phi)$.

Hence $NP' = 2r.\tan \frac{1}{2}\theta = 2r.\tan (45 - \frac{1}{2}\phi)$.

But $NP = r.\theta^c$, where θ^c is in circular measure (radians).

Thus, when θ is very small, that is, when P is very near the pole, $\tan \frac{1}{2}\theta = \frac{1}{2} \tan \theta$ (very nearly), and $2r.\tan \frac{1}{2}\theta = r.\tan \theta = r.\theta^c$

(very nearly). The distance of P' from N is thus very nearly equal to the distance of P from N. Over a very small area near the centre of the projection, therefore, *distances measured from the centre* are very nearly true, when compared with corresponding distances on the 'generating' globe.

When θ increases, however, distances from the centre of the projection are exaggerated, but not to the same extent as on the *gnomonic*. Rather larger areas can thus be satisfactorily mapped on the *stereographic* than on the *gnomonic*.

An indication of the exaggeration in radial distances is given in the following table, which gives corresponding values of θ^c and $2.\tan\frac{1}{2}\theta$:

$\theta°$	θ^c	$2.\tan\frac{1}{2}\theta$	$\theta°$	θ^c	$2.\tan\frac{1}{2}\theta$
5	0·0873	0·0874	35	0·6109	0·6306
10	0·1745	0·1750	40	0·6981	0·7280
15	0·2618	0·2634	45	0·7854	0·8284
20	0·3491	0·3526	50	0·8727	0·9326
25	0·4363	0·4434	55	0·9599	1·0412
30	0·5236	0·5358	60	1·0472	1·1548

In the *polar* case the parallels of latitude are projected as circles, described about the pole as centre. The meridians of longitude are projected as radii, uniformly spaced at their correct angular intervals.

On the globe the length of the parallel in latitude ϕ is $2\pi r.\cos\phi$; on the projection the length of this same parallel is $4\pi r.\tan(45-\frac{1}{2}\phi)$. An indication of the exaggeration in the scale of the parallels can thus be obtained by comparing $\cos\phi$ and $2.\tan(45-\frac{1}{2}\phi)$ for selected values of ϕ, as in the following table:

$\phi°$	$\cos\phi$	$2.\tan(45-\frac{1}{2}\phi)$	$\phi°$	$\cos\phi$	$2.\tan(45-\frac{1}{2}\phi)$
85	0·0872	0·0874	55	0·5736	0·6306
80	0·1736	0·1750	50	0·6428	0·7280
75	0·2588	0·2634	45	0·7071	0·8284
70	0·3420	0·3526	40	0·7660	0·9326
65	0·4226	0·4434	35	0·8192	1·0412
60	0·5000	0·5358	30	0·8660	1·1548

Quite clearly, the *scale along the parallels* also increases away from the centre of the projections. (These tables should be compared with those given for the *gnomonic*.)

It will now be instructive to compare, for any given *point* on the projection, the *scale along the meridian* with the *scale along the parallel*.

Consider the point where any selected meridian intersects the parallel in latitude ϕ. On the projection the length of the complete parallel is $4\pi r.\tan\ (45-\tfrac{1}{2}\phi)$; on the globe the length of this same parallel is $2\pi r.\cos\ \phi$.

The *exaggeration* of the scale along the projected parallel may therefore be expressed:

$$\frac{2.\tan\ (45-\tfrac{1}{2}\phi)}{\cos\ \phi} \quad\dots\dots\dots\dots\dots\dots\dots\dots\dots\text{(i)}$$

Now consider two points on the selected meridian, one on each side of the parallel ϕ, and both equally close to it. Let the latitudes of these points be ϕ' and ϕ''. The distance between them on the projection is $2r.\tan\ (45-\tfrac{1}{2}\phi')-2r.\tan\ (45-\tfrac{1}{2}\phi'')$, whereas the distance between them on the globe is $2\pi r.\dfrac{(\phi'-\phi'')}{360}$

The *exaggeration* of the scale along the projected meridian, between ϕ' and ϕ'', may therefore be expressed:

$$\frac{\tan\ (45-\tfrac{1}{2}\phi')-\tan\ (45-\tfrac{1}{2}\phi'')}{\pi.\dfrac{(\phi'-\phi'')}{360}} \quad\dots\dots\dots\dots\dots\text{(ii)}$$

By bringing ϕ' and ϕ'' very close together, it is possible to approximate to the actual conditions at the selected *point* on the parallel ϕ, and hence to compare the exaggeration in the scale along the parallel (i) with the exaggeration in the scale along the meridian (ii) at that point. The following results have been obtained by using 7-figure tables in the calculations:

	$\phi°$	$\phi'°$	$\phi''°$	(i)	(ii)
(A)	30°	30° 2′	29° 58′	1·3333	1·3333
(B)	45°	45° 2′	44° 58′	1·1716	1·1716
(C)	60°	60° 2′	59° 58′	1·0718	1·0718

The results are sufficiently conclusive to show that, although the *actual* scale varies from one latitude to another, at any *point* the scale along the parallel is equal to the scale along the meridian. As a result of this '*equal-stretching*', the *stereographic* possesses an important property, namely, *shape is preserved at a point*; the projection is therefore said to be *orthomorphic*. In practice the property of orthomorphism (true representation of shape) can be extended to *small areas*; for example, a *small* square anywhere on the globe would be projected as a square, but the size of the projected square would depend on its position with reference to the centre of the projection. On account of the variation in the actual scale, from one latitude to another, however, orthomorphism cannot be extended to large areas. The shape of a small area is virtually preserved, but the shape of a large area is not.

Although, for the sake of simplicity in the calculations, the orthomorphic property was considered only in the *polar* case of the *stereographic*, it is equally true in the other cases, and for this reason the *stereographic* is often called the *Zenithal Orthomorphic Projection* (cf. *Cylindrical Orthomorphic* on p. 37, and *Conical Orthomorphic* on pp. 104 and 107).

In the *stereographic*, only those great circles which pass through *both* the point of origin and the point of contact of the plane of projection with the globe are projected as straight lines. The meridians in the *polar* case are great circles which fall into this class; so also are the equator and the central meridian in the *equatorial* case.

Summary of Properties. In many respects the *stereographic* is more serviceable than the *gnomonic*, especially when rather larger areas are mapped, for the distortion away from the centre is not so marked; it is possible, for example, to project a complete hemisphere, but the projection of such a large area is of very limited use. The really distinctive property of the projection is its orthomorphism.

Limitations. The increase in the scale, away from the centre, though less than in the *gnomonic*, is nevertheless appreciable, but the difficulties introduced by the varying scale are to some extent offset by the orthomorphic properties of the projection.

Construction. With centre N, the projection of the North Pole, describe circles of radii $2r.\tan(45 - \frac{1}{2}\phi)$, where ϕ is any required angle of latitude. These circles are the projected parallels of latitude. The meridians can now be drawn, as straight lines, radiating from N at their true angular intervals.

The *equatorial* and *oblique* cases are discussed on p. 78 *et seq.*

THE ORTHOGRAPHIC PROJECTION

The point of origin is at infinity, and the plane of projection is tangential in any desired position; so *polar, equatorial,* and *oblique* cases are all possible. The resulting projection is, as it were, a photographic view of a distant globe.

Fig. 5 represents a section through the centre of the globe, at right angles to the plane of projection; *P'* is the *orthographic* projection of the point *P*.

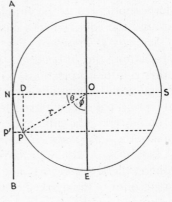

Let the radius of the globe be *r*, and let the point *P* be in latitude ϕ; that is, $\angle EOP = \phi°$. Let $\angle PON = \theta$; then $\theta = (90-\phi)$.

Hence $NP' = DP = r.\sin \theta = r.\cos \phi$.

But $NP = r.\theta^c$, where θ^c is in circular measure (radians).

Thus, when θ is very small, that is, when *P* is very near the

FIG. 5

pole, $\sin \theta = \theta^c$ (very nearly). The distance of *P'* from *N* is thus very nearly equal to the distance of *P* from *N*. Over a small area near the centre of the projection, therefore, *distances measured from the centre* are very nearly true, when compared with corresponding distances on the 'generating' globe.

When θ increases, however, $\sin \theta$ becomes appreciably less than θ^c, as the following table shows:

$\theta°$	θ^c	$\sin \theta$	$\theta°$	θ^c	$\sin \theta$
5	0·0873	0·0872	35	0·6109	0·5736
10	0·1745	0·1736	40	0·6981	0·6428
15	0·2618	0·2588	45	0·7854	0·7071
20	0·3491	0·3420	50	0·8727	0·7660
25	0·4363	0·4226	55	0·9599	0·8192
30	0·5236	0·5000	60	1·0472	0·8660

For a small area near the centre of the projection, therefore, the representation is reasonably accurate, but away from the centre, the *radial scale* decreases rapidly, and distortion is soon apparent.

In the *polar* case the parallels of latitude are projected as circles, described about the pole as centre. The meridians of longitude are projected as radii, uniformly spaced at their correct angular intervals.

On the globe the length of the parallel in latitude ϕ is $2\pi r.\cos \phi$; on the projection the length of this same parallel is also $2\pi r.\cos \phi$. The scale along the parallels is therefore always correct. Since the meridian scale decreases away from the centre, distortion of shape and area is inevitable, and is particularly pronounced around the edges when a complete hemisphere is shown.

Summary of Properties. For a *small* area near the centre of the projection, the *orthographic* is not markedly different from the other zenithal projections, but when large areas are mapped, the radial scale diminishes away from the centre. As the parallels are projected at their true lengths, distortion of shape becomes pronounced. The infinite perspective embodied in the projection makes the *orthographic* suitable for star charts.

Limitations. Although frequently used for the complete hemisphere, the *orthographic* is not really suitable for such a large area, on account of the marked distortion of shape, caused by the great inequality in the scales in different directions. In the popular mind, however, this disadvantage is offset to some extent because the general effect is that of viewing a distant globe, and there is accordingly some pretence to reality.

Construction. With centre N, the projection of the North Pole, describe circles of radii $r.\cos \phi$, where ϕ is any required angle of latitude. These circles are the projected parallels of latitude. The meridians can now be drawn, as straight lines, radiating from N at their true angular intervals.

The *equatorial* and *oblique* cases are discussed on p. 88 *et seq.*

APPROXIMATE 'EQUIDISTANT' PROJECTION

The essential characteristics of the perspective (or geometrical) zenithal projections depend upon the distance of the point of origin from the plane of projection, for this determines the *radial scale.* The point of origin may be placed in any arbitrarily determined position, but the question of the relative advantages and disadvantages of the resulting projection then arises. Each of the three perspective zenithals already described has one salient property, which gives the projection some distinctive advantage, whatever other limitations may thereby be implicitly enforced. Thus, in the case of the *gnomonic*, all great circles are projected as straight lines; the *stereographic* is an orthomorphic projection; the *orthographic* gives, in effect, a distant view of the globe. Each projection can therefore be used to advantage for a specific purpose, but none of the three is really suitable for a general map of a large area.

The following example illustrates how another specific principle may be embodied, so far as is possible, in the construction of a zenithal perspective projection. In the first instance the purpose is to project a complete hemisphere in such a way that radial distances suffer the minimum distortion. In other words, the purpose is to devise an approximate 'equidistant' projection (see p. 21).

In *Fig. 6*, which represents a section through the centre of the globe, at right angles to the plane of projection, the position of

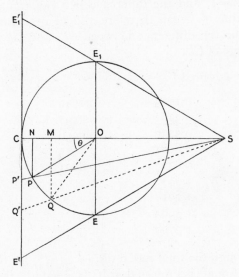

FIG. 6

the point of origin (S) is such that the *radial distance* (CE'), on the projection, is equal to the *arc distance* (CE), on the globe, when $\angle COE = 90°$. Thus, when C is one of the poles, E is on the equator, and CE is the meridian distance from the pole to the equator.

Let r be the radius of the globe, and let the distance OS be x.

Then, in the similar triangles SOE and SCE', $\dfrac{r}{CE'} = \dfrac{x}{r+x}$

whence $x = \dfrac{r^2}{CE' - r}$

When $r = 1$, $CE = 1·5708$, $CE' = 1·5708$, and $x = 1·7520$.

Therefore $\angle CSE' = \tan^{-1} \dfrac{1·5708}{2·7520} = 20° \ 43'$ (very nearly).

Let P be a point on the surface of the globe such that
$$\angle PON = \theta; \text{ then } PN = r.\sin\theta, \text{ and } ON = r.\cos\theta.$$

Thus, in the similar triangles SNP and SCP', $\dfrac{CP'}{NP} = \dfrac{CS}{NS}$, and

$$CP' = \frac{2 \cdot 7520 \sin \theta}{1 \cdot 7520 + \cos \theta}, \text{ when } r = 1.$$

By giving different values to θ, between $0°$ and $90°$, the projected *radial distance* (CP'), corresponding to any given position of P, can be determined. The *arc distance* (CP) on the globe is equal to θ^c, when $r = 1$, and the difference between CP' and CP, for any given value of θ, can therefore also be determined. In the following table the difference between CP' and CP is expressed as a percentage of CP:

$\theta°$	CP	CP'	$\left(\dfrac{CP'-CP}{CP}\right)$ %
10	0·1745	0·1745	0·0
20	0·3491	0·3497	0·2
30	0·5236	0·5256	0·4
40	0·6981	0·7025	0·6
50	0·8727	0·8801	0·8
60	1·0472	1·0583	1·0
70	1·2217	1·2350	1·1
80	1·3963	1·4071	0·8
90	1·5708	1·5708	0·0

Thus, although the total radial distance (CP') for the complete hemisphere ($\theta = 90$) is projected at its true length, the *radial scale* is not everywhere strictly correct; but the percentage error in the above table scarcely exceeds 1 at any point, and is generally much less. The figures tabulated under CP and CP', however, give the total distances from the centre of the projection; to obtain an indication of the radial scale in any part of the projection it is therefore necessary to resort to a process of subtraction, as follows:

Difference θ	Difference CP (globe)	Difference CP' (projection)	Scale error (projection) %
10–20	0·1746	0·1752	0·3
20–30	0·1746	0·1759	0·6
30–40	0·1746	0·1769	1·3
40–50	0·1746	0·1776	1·7
50–60	0·1746	0·1782	2·1
60–70	0·1746	0·1767	1·2
70–80	0·1746	0·1721	−1·4
80–90	0·1746	0·1637	−6·2

It is now clear that the projection is by no means strictly '*equidistant*', for the percentage error in the radial scale near the edge of the hemisphere is considerable; over most of the area, however, the approximation is quite good. It is extremely doubtful if a perspective projection of this kind is of any real value, for the simple reason that it cannot achieve the one property demanded of it, namely, a true radial scale. By altering the position of the point of origin, the radial distance (CP') can be 'corrected' so as to equal the arc distance (CP) for any specified value of θ, but it is not possible to produce a truly *equidistant* zenithal projection by purely perspective methods (see p. 21).

APPROXIMATE 'EQUAL-AREA' PROJECTION

The following example illustrates how the '*equal-area*' principle may be embodied in the construction of a zenithal perspective projection. The purpose now is the correct representation of *area*, regardless of shape and other factors.

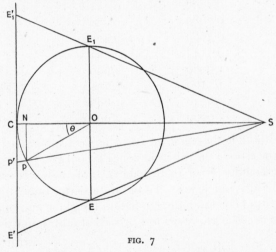

FIG. 7

In *Fig.* 7, which represents a section through the centre of the globe, at right angles to the plane of projection, the position of the point of origin (S) is such that the area of a hemisphere on the globe is correctly represented on the projection by the circle whose radius is CE'.

The area of the hemisphere is $2\pi r^2$; the area of the circle on the projection is $\pi(CE')^2$. Therefore $CE' = r.\sqrt{2}$.

Let $OS = y$; then $y = \dfrac{r^2}{CE' - r}$

When $r=1$, $y=2\cdot4143$, and $\angle CSE'=\tan^{-1}\dfrac{1\cdot4142}{3\cdot4143}$

$$=22°\ 30'\ \text{(very nearly)}.$$

Let P be a point on the surface of the globe such that

$$\angle PON=\theta,\ \text{then}\ CP'=\frac{3\cdot4143\ \sin\ \theta}{2\cdot4143+\cos\ \theta}$$

On the projection, the area of the circle of radius CP', is $\pi(CP')^2$; on the globe, the area of the corresponding zone is $2\pi.(1-\cos\ \theta)$, when $r=1$.

The following table shows, for selected values of θ, the relation between the *areas* of different zones on the globe, and the *areas* of the corresponding circles on the projection. As π is a common factor, it has been ignored in making the calculations.

$\theta°$	(G) area on globe (from pole)	(P) area on projection (from centre)	$\dfrac{(P)-(G)}{(G)}$ %
10	0·0304	0·0304	0·0
20	0·1206	0·1212	0·5
30	0·2680	0·2708	1·0
40	0·4680	0·4768	1·8
50	0·7144	0·7317	2·4
60	1·0000	1·0290	2·9
70	1·3160	1·3546	2·9
80	1·6528	1·6866	2·0
90	2·0000	2·0000	0·0

Thus, although the total *area* of the hemisphere is projected correctly, the *areas* of the different zones are not everywhere correct; but the percentage error in the above table nowhere exceeds 3, and is generally much less. To obtain a better indication of the relative areas of corresponding zones on the globe and on the projection, it is necessary to resort to a process of subtraction as follows:

Difference θ	Difference (G)	Difference (P)	Error on Projection %
10–20	0·0902	0·0908	0·7
20–30	0·1474	0·1496	1·5
30–40	0·2000	0·2060	3·0
40–50	0·2464	0·2549	3·5
50–60	0·2856	0·2973	4·1
60–70	0·3160	0·3256	3·0
70–80	0·3368	0·3320	—1·4
80–90	0·3472	0·3134	—9·7

The projection is clearly not strictly 'equal-area', but over the greater part of the hemisphere the approximation is tolerable. Here, again, is a perspective projection of doubtful value, for the 'equal-area' property cannot be accurately preserved. By altering the position of the point of origin, the greatest possible degree of accuracy can be made to coincide with any selected zone, but it is quite impossible to maintain even fair accuracy over a large area. In short, it is not possible to produce an *equal-area* zenithal projection by purely perspective methods (see p. 23).

NON-PERSPECTIVE

The projections already discussed have all been developed by geometrical methods, namely, by 'rays' radiating from a point of origin, and falling upon a suitably placed plane. In the present section, two important *non-perspective* projections are discussed; they cannot be regarded as projected by 'rays' from any one point of origin, but they can be regarded as 'modified' zenithals, for they conform to the zenithal type.

THE ZENITHAL EQUIDISTANT PROJECTION

In this projection the *radial scale* is adjusted so that every point on the projection lies at its correct distance from the centre. Thus, in *Fig. 8*, CP' is made equal to the arc CP for all values of θ. The projected position of P, namely, P', therefore lies at a distance of $r.\theta^c$ from the centre, and, as in the case of the perspective zenithals, the direction of P' from the centre of the map is true.

In the *polar* case, the point C represents one of the poles, and the $\angle COP$ is thus the co-latitude of the point P; that is, if P is in latitude ϕ, $\theta = (90-\phi)$. The parallels of latitude are thus projected as concentric circles, of radii $r.\theta^c$, or $r.(90-\phi)^c$, while the meridians are projected as radii of these circles, and correctly spaced at their true angular intervals.

The *scale along the meridians*, that is, radially from the centre, is everywhere correct, and it is

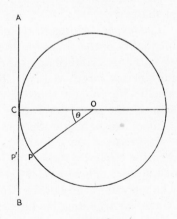

FIG. 8

in respect of this property that the projection is said to be *'equidistant'*. The scale along the parallels, however, is not correct, as the following calculations show.

In latitude ϕ, the radius of the parallel on the globe is $r.\cos\phi$; on the projection, the radius of this same parallel is $r.(90-\phi)^c$. As the lengths of the parallels are proportional to their radii, it is sufficient to compare the radii when r is equal to 1.

Lat. ϕ	Cos ϕ	$(90-\phi)^c$	Lat. ϕ	Cos ϕ	$(90-\phi)^c$
90	0·0000	0·0000	40	0·7660	0·8727
80	0·1736	0·1745	30	0·8660	1·0472
70	0·3420	0·3491	20	0·9397	1·2217
60	0·5000	0·5236	10	0·9848	1·3963
50	0·6428	0·6981	0	1·0000	1·5708

Thus, away from the centre of the projections, the *scale along the parallels* increases somewhat rapidly, and is very exaggerated around the edge of the complete hemisphere. As the scale along the meridians is everywhere correct, areas are accordingly exaggerated on the projection.

Summary of Properties. For a *small* area near the centre of the projection, the representation is very satisfactory, and in one particular respect, there is undoubted merit, namely, that distances from the centre are always true. Provided the area is not too large, the projection makes a very serviceable general map; but when distances from the centre become considerable, there is pronounced exaggeration of area and appreciable distortion of shape.

Limitations. Although the radial scale always remains true, the inequality of the scales in different directions produces distortion of both area and shape, and the projection is thus not really suitable for large areas. If, however, a map is required for the specific purpose of showing 'equal distance' from a particular 'centre', the projection can be used to good effect, for the required 'centre' can be made the centre of the projection.

Construction. With centre N, the projection of the North Pole, describe circles of radii $r.(90-\phi)^c$, where ϕ is the required angle of latitude. These circles are the projected parallels of latitude. The meridians can now be drawn, as straight lines, radiating from N at their true angular intervals.

The *equatorial* and *oblique* cases are discussed on pp. 92 and 100.

THE ZENITHAL EQUAL-AREA PROJECTION

In this projection the *radial scale* is adjusted so that *areas* are everywhere correctly represented. The only consideration, therefore, is that *areas* shall be strictly comparable over the entire projection. In the process of adjustment, *shape* and *distance* may both become distorted, but that is of no significance for the present purpose.

In *Fig. 9*, which represents a section through the centre of the 'generating' globe, at right angles to the plane of projection (*AB*), P is a point on the globe such that $\angle PON = \theta$.

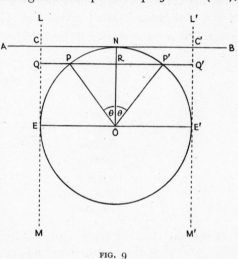

For the present, the point N represents the North Pole, but, if need be, it could represent any other point without invalidating the argument. $LMM'L'$ is a cylinder which touches the globe along the circumference (EE'), the plane of which is parallel to the plane of projection; the axis of the cylinder is therefore coincident with the line ON.

FIG. 9

The area of the zone $PEE'P'$, on the globe, is equal to the area of the zone $QEE'Q'$, on the cylinder, since both zones are contained between the same planes (EE' and QQ'), both of which are perpendicular to the axis of the cylinder. Let r be the radius of the globe:

area of zone $QEE'Q' = 2\pi r.(QE) = 2\pi r^2.\cos\theta$
area of zone $CEE'C' = 2\pi r.(CE) = 2\pi r^2$
area of zone $CQQ'C' = 2\pi r^2(1 - \cos\theta)$.

The *area* of the zone PNP', on the globe, is thus $2\pi r^2(1 - \cos\theta)$. But the zone PNP' is projected as a circle; let the radius of this circle be R; then its *area* will be $\pi.R^2$.

Thus, $\pi.R^2 = 2\pi r^2(1 - \cos\theta)$; whence $R = r.\sqrt{2(1 - \cos\theta)}$.

In the *polar* case, when N is the North Pole, and P is in latitude ϕ, $\theta = (90 - \phi)$; hence $\cos\theta = \sin\phi$.

The parallels of latitude are thus projected as concentric circles of radii $r.\sqrt{2(1-\sin\phi)}$; and the meridians radiate from the centre of the projection at their true angular intervals.

The length of the parallel in latitude ϕ is $2\pi r.\cos\phi$; on the projection the length of this same parallel is $2\pi r.\sqrt{2(1-\sin\phi)}$. To compare the scales along the parallels, on the globe and on the projection, it is therefore sufficient to compare $\cos\phi$ and $\sqrt{2(1-\sin\phi)}$. The distance of the parallel in latitude ϕ from the pole of the globe is $r.(90-\phi)^c$; the distance of the same parallel from the centre of the projection is $r.\sqrt{2(1-\sin\phi)}$.

The following table gives the relation between $\cos\phi$, $\sqrt{2(1-\sin\phi)}$ and $(90-\phi)^c$, for selected values of ϕ:

Lat. ϕ	Cos ϕ	$\sqrt{2(1-\sin\phi)}$	$(90-\phi)^c$
80	0·1736	0·1743	0·1745
70	0·3420	0·3473	0·3491
60	0·5000	0·5177	0·5236
50	0·6428	0·6841	0·6981
40	0·7660	0·8452	0·8727
30	0·8660	1·0000	1·0472
20	0·9397	1·1470	1·2217
10	0·9848	1·2860	1·3963
0	1·0000	1·4142	1·5708

It is clear that the scale along the parallels is everywhere too great, and that the parallels are all too close to the centre. To obtain a fair indication of the scale along the meridians, however, it is necessary to resort to a process of subtraction, as follows:

Difference ϕ	Difference $\sqrt{2(1-\sin\phi)}$	Difference $(90-\phi)^c$
90–80	0·1743	0·1745
80–70	0·1730	0·1745
70–60	0·1704	0·1745
60–50	0·1664	0·1745
50–40	0·1611	0·1745
40–30	0·1548	0·1745
30–20	0·1470	0·1745
20–10	0·1390	0·1745
10– 0	0·1282	0·1745

It is now apparent that the scale along the meridians is everywhere too small, and that the scale becomes increasingly diminished away from the centre. This is only to be expected, for the scale along the parallels is everywhere too great, and the *equal-area* property can therefore only be preserved by a compensatory diminution in the scale along the meridians. Away from the centre, *shape* becomes progressively distorted, due to the inequality of the scales in different directions.

Summary of Properties. For a *small* area near the centre of the projection, the representation is very satisfactory; and *areas* are always true. The *equal-area* property makes the projection particularly valuable. Moreover, provided the area is not too large, the projection makes an admirable general map; even in the case of large areas, the *equal-area* property may outweigh other considerations.

Limitations. Apart from the one property of equal-area, which remains true over the entire projection, there is appreciable distortion away from the centre; in a sense, 'radial compression' is accompanied by 'tangential stretching', and when these distortions become appreciable, shape becomes grossly deformed. In projecting very large parts of the earth's surface, however, distortion is inevitable, and provided the centre is carefully chosen, there are certain advantages in the use of the *zenithal equal-area* projection in such circumstances.

Construction. With centre N, the projection of the North Pole, describe circles of radii $r.\sqrt{2(1-\sin\phi)}$, where ϕ is the required angle of latitude. These circles are the projected parallels of latitude. The meridians can now be drawn, as straight lines, radiating from N at their true angular intervals.

The *equatorial* and *oblique* cases are discussed on pp. 94 and 100.

TRANSFORMATION IN ZENITHAL PROJECTION

IN the case of the *polar zenithals*, it has now been shown that when r is the radius of the 'generating' globe, the distance of a point in latitude ϕ from the centre of the projection is given by the following expressions:

Gnomonic:	$r.\cot\phi$
Stereographic:	$2r.\tan(45-\tfrac{1}{2}\phi)$
Orthographic:	$r.\cos\phi$
Equidistant:	$r.(90-\phi)^{c}$
Equal Area:	$r.\sqrt{2(1-\sin\phi)}$.

From these expressions it is possible to determine the spacing between the parallels of latitude on the different *polar zenithals*, and hence to compare the *radial scales* of the different projections. This is illustrated in *Fig. 10*, in which the different projections have all been developed from the same globe. Near the centres of the projections there is apparently very little difference in the scales, but it must be appreciated that even small differences may

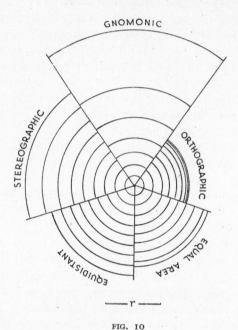

FIG. 10

ZENITHAL PROJECTIONS COMPARED (POLAR CASES)
The parallels of latitude are shown at intervals of 10°.

alter the appearance and usefulness of *large-scale* maps to a considerable extent. It is important, therefore, that subtle distinctions, although often obscured on *small-scale* maps, should be thoroughly understood, for, in the case of small areas, it is in the large-scale representation that the distinctive qualities of the different projections become apparent. When large areas are mapped, the differences are at once obvious, even on small-scale maps.

In *Fig. 11* the *radial distance* from the centre of the various zenithal projections is plotted against the *angle subtended* at the centre of the 'generating' globe. Here, again, it will be noticed that when the angle subtended is very small, one projection apparently differs but little from another. As the angle increases, however, the differences become clearly marked, and each projection is seen to have its own characteristic radial scale. In the case of the *equidistant zenithal* the graph is a straight line, for the radial distance, by definition, is directly proportional to the angle subtended; that is the basis of '*equidistance*'. The graphs for the *gnomonic* and *stereographic* projections show that their radial

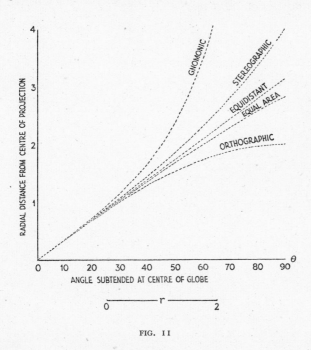

FIG. 11

scales become increasingly exaggerated as the subtended angle increases; in the case of the *gnomonic* the exaggeration is more pronounced than in the case of the *stereographic*. The graphs for the *equal-area* and *orthographic* projections show that their radial scales suffer progressive diminution as the subtended angle increases. The graphs demonstrate, in fact, what has already been shown in another way by the several tables to which reference has been made from time to time.

The only essential difference between the various zenithal projections, whether perspective or non-perspective, lies, therefore, in their different *radial scales*. Merely by modifying the radial scale it is possible to transform one zenithal projection into another. In the *equatorial* and *oblique* cases, some projections are more easily constructed than others; it is thus sometimes convenient to construct one of the simpler types, and then to transform it to the required type by appropriate modification of the radial scale. The radial scale of the *polar zenithals* is the scale along the meridians; in the *equatorial* and *oblique* cases the radial scale cannot be thus easily related to either the meridians or the parallels, for these lines are not, in general, radial to the projections (see p. 98 *et seq.*).

CHAPTER III

CYLINDRICAL PROJECTIONS

PROJECTIONS of this class can be visualized as made on a cylinder, which is then cut along a convenient line parallel to the axis, and opened out flat. In the *normal* position the axis of the cylinder is coincident with the axis of the 'generating' globe; the cylinder may then be regarded as either touching the globe along the equator, or intersecting the globe along two symmetrically placed parallels of latitude. In the *transverse* position the cylinder may be regarded as touching the globe along the great circle formed by two selected opposite meridians.

As in the case of the zenithals, perspective and non-perspective projections are possible.

Several features are characteristic of all *normal* cylindrical projections:

(i) The parallels of latitude are projected as parallel straight lines, all of equal length, and one of which (depending on the particular projection) is correctly divided, on the scale of the 'generating' globe, for the points of intersection with the meridians.

(ii) The meridians of longitude are also projected as parallel straight lines, all of equal length, and all equally spaced.

(iii) All meridians intersect all parallels at right angles.

(iv) The complete projections are therefore essentially rectangular.

Since the parallels of latitude are all projected equal in length, it is evident that there must be considerable distortion of scale along those parallels which are at some distance from the '*standard*' parallel. On the other hand, the scale along every meridian can be made correct, for the meridians are all projected equal in length, as on the globe. The rectangular intersection of parallels and meridians, it should be noted, is true to the globe, if the dimensional aspect is ignored.

THE SIMPLE PERSPECTIVE CYLINDRICAL

In this case the 'generating' globe may be regarded as fitting inside a cylinder; the projection is then made geometrically from the centre of the globe on to the cylinder, which is afterwards opened out flat.

In *Fig. 12*, the cylinder $(ABB'A')$ touches the globe along the equator (EE'); the axis of the globe (NS) is therefore coincident with the axis of the cylinder. Let P be a point on the surface of the globe in latitude ϕ, and let P' be its projection on the cylinder. Then $E'P' = r.\tan \phi$, and $E'P = r.\phi^c$.

When ϕ is very small, that is, for points near the equator, $\tan \phi = \phi^c$ (very nearly), and distances measured away from the equator, both northwards and southwards, are reasonably true to the globe. But when ϕ is large, that is, for points in high latitudes, $\tan \phi$ becomes progressively greater than ϕ^c, so distances

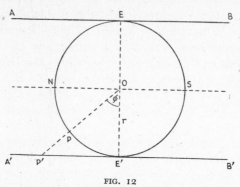

FIG. 12

SIMPLE PERSPECTIVE CYLINDRICAL PROJECTION

measured away from the equator are exaggerated, and the exaggeration increases with increasing distance from the equator.

Except at the equator, where they are correct, distances measured along the parallels are also exaggerated, for all the parallels are projected equal in length to the equator. On the globe the length of the parallel in latitude ϕ is $2\pi r.\cos \phi$; on the projection the length of this same parallel is $2\pi r$.

Thus $\dfrac{\text{length of projected parallel}}{\text{length of parallel on globe}} = \dfrac{2\pi r}{2\pi r.\cos \phi} = \sec \phi$.

The parallel in latitude ϕ is therefore 'magnified' *sec* ϕ times. At the equator, $\phi = 0°$, and $\sec \phi = 1$; so the equator is represented correctly. In latitude $60°$ the projected parallel is 'stretched' to twice its true length; in latitude $75\frac{1}{2}°$ the projected parallel is 'stretched' to about four times its true length. The poles cannot be projected, of course, in the *equatorial* case.

This projection is really of very little use, but it does serve to illustrate some of the problems connected with cylindrical projection.

THE PLATE CARRÉE

This is a simple non-perspective cylindrical projection. The equator is projected as a straight line, of correct length, and accurately divided for the points of intersection with the meridians, which are projected as straight lines, also of correct length, and perpendicular to the equator. The meridians are correctly divided for the points of intersection with the parallels, which are therefore straight lines, parallel to the equator.

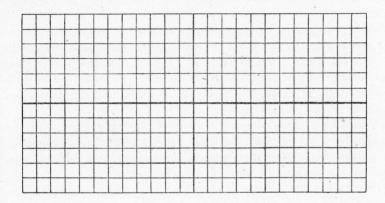

FIG. 13

PLATE CARRÉE

(SIMPLE NON-PERSPECTIVE CYLINDRICAL PROJECTION)

Meridians and parallels at intervals of 15°.

The complete projection is shown in *Fig. 13*, in which both meridians and parallels are spaced at intervals of 15°, so dividing the projection into a number of true squares, a feature which gives point to the name of this particular projection.

The scale along the equator and all meridians is true to the globe from which the projection has been developed; but along all other parallels the scale is too great, the exaggeration increasing markedly away from the equator. On the globe the length of the parallel in latitude ϕ is $2\pi r.\cos \phi$; on the projection the length of every parallel is $2\pi r$. The length of the projected parallel ϕ is therefore magnified $sec\ \phi$ times its true length. Since there is nothing to compensate for this glaring exaggeration in the scale along the parallels, the projection is of limited use, except for a relatively narrow belt near the equator. The following table gives the value of sec ϕ for selected values of ϕ:

$\phi°$	sec ϕ	$\phi°$	sec ϕ
0	1·0000	50	1·5557
10	1·0154	60	2·0000
20	1·0642	70	2·9238
30	1·1547	80	5·7588
40	1·3054	90	∞

This pronounced exaggeration in the scale along the parallels, accompanied by correct scale along all meridians, necessarily entails pronounced exaggeration of *areas* away from the equator.

Summary of Properties. The scale along the equator and all meridians is true; but the scale along other parallels is magnified *sec ϕ* times. Purely with reference to distances measured at right angles to the equator, that is, along the meridians, this projection may be styled 'equidistant'.

Limitations. Away from the equator the exaggeration in the scale along the parallels becomes very marked, and, except for a narrow belt along the equator, the projection is of little use, for there is nothing by way of compensation.

Construction. Draw the equator true to scale, as a straight line, and divide it correctly for the meridian intersections. Draw the meridians true to scale, as straight lines, at right angles to the equator. Draw the parallels of latitude at their true distance from the equator; for example, divide one of the meridians correctly for the points of intersection of the parallels, and through these points draw lines parallel to the equator.

CASSINI'S PROJECTION

This is an example of the *transverse* application of the *Plate Carrée*; that is, the cylinder may be regarded as touching the globe along the great circle formed by two selected opposite meridians.

In the complete projection the equator and the selected pair of meridians are projected as perpendicular straight lines, and both are made true to scale. All other parallels of latitude and meridians of longitude are projected as curves, which are conditioned by the requirement that distances at right angles to the projected 'central' meridian are made true.

This projection is of value for mapping an area which has only a small extent in longitude, for then the representation can be made sensibly true in every respect. It is for this reason that

Cassini's Projection has been used for certain maps of the Ordnance Survey of England. The whole area included in the survey is mapped with reference to one 'central' meridian, and when the complete map is cut into a number of sheets, the sheets all fit together exactly. As the separate sheets are rectangular, however, they are not, in general, bounded by meridians and parallels.

In the case of a country of the size and shape of England, it is possible to achieve excellent representation on this projection. The scale along the 'central' meridian is true, as also is the scale everywhere at right angles to that meridian. Since there is no very great extent in longitude, there can be no appreciable exaggeration in the scale in a direction parallel to, but away from, the 'central' meridian. Moreover, the intersections of the parallels and meridians are practically rectangular over the whole of such a small area. Thus the representation is virtually perfect in every respect. (For some purposes, however, it is desirable to base the projection of small areas upon other principles, even if the differences are seemingly insignificant by most practical standards. See p. 41.)

Maps of the Ordnance Survey, especially those required for military purposes, are frequently overprinted with a rectangular *grid*, that is, a network of numbered squares to facilitate the identification of any required point. The 'north-south' lines of this grid will not, in general, be true north-south lines, for only the central meridian is projected as a straight line. Further, with large-scale maps of this kind, magnetic bearings often figure prominently in the use that is made of the maps in the field. Thus, when refinement is required, there is a very real distinction between *true* north, *grid* north, and *magnetic* north.

GALL'S PROJECTION

In this projection the cylinder may be regarded as intersecting the globe along the parallels of latitude 45°N. and 45°S. The projection is then made *stereographically*, as shown in *Fig. 14*, which represents a section through the centre of the globe, at right angles to the plane of the equator. Each meridian is projected with reference to its own particular point of origin, which lies on the equator of the 'generating' globe, opposite the meridian which is to be projected. Thus, the point of origin for the projection of every point along the meridian in longitude θ° is the point of intersection of the meridian in longitude $(\theta+180)$° with the equator.

3

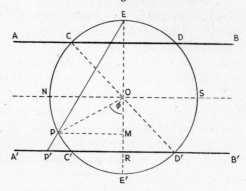

FIG. 14
GALL'S CYLINDRICAL PROJECTION

Let P be a point in latitude ϕ, and let P' be its projection on the cylinder; let PM be drawn perpendicular to EE'.

Then $PM = r.\sin \phi$; $EM = r + r.\cos \phi$; $ER = r + r.\cos 45°$.

In the similar triangles EPM and $EP'R$, $\dfrac{P'R}{PM} = \dfrac{ER}{EM}$

whence $P'R = \dfrac{r.\sin \phi \ (1 + \cos 45°)}{1 + \cos \phi}$

The true arc distance on the globe, corresponding to $P'R$, is $r.\phi^c$, and it is therefore possible to make a direct comparison, as in the following table, where $r = 1$:

$\phi°$	ϕ^c	$P'R$	$\phi°$	ϕ^c	$P'R$
10	0·1745	0·1493	60	1·0472	0·9856
20	0·3491	0·3010	70	1·2217	1·1953
30	0·5236	0·4574	80	1·3963	1·4324
40	0·6981	0·6213	90	1·5708	1·7071
50	0·8727	0·7960			

The table makes it clear that, over by far the greater part of the projection, the parallels of latitude are too close to the equator. To obtain an indication of the meridian scale, however, it is necessary to resort to a process of subtraction, as follows:

Differences

$\phi°$	ϕ^c	$P'R$	$\phi°$	ϕ^c	$P'R$
0–10	0·1745	0·1493	50–60	0·1745	0·1896
10–20	0·1745	0·1517	60–70	0·1745	0·2097
20–30	0·1745	0·1564	70–80	0·1745	0·2371
30–40	0·1745	0·1639	80–90	0·1745	0·2747
40–50	0·1745	0·1747			

It is now clear that the meridian scale is too small near the equator, and too large near the poles; only in the immediate vicinity of the parallels 45°N. and 45°S. is the meridian scale correct.

The two tables show that there is a difference between the *scale* along the meridians, and the *distance* of the parallels from the equator. Thus, although the projected parallels in latitudes 60° and 70° are both too close to the equator, the distance between them is actually too great; that is, although they are both too close to the equator, the meridian scale in that vicinity is too great. The mere fact that a parallel is projected too close to the equator does not necessarily mean, therefore, that the meridian scale at that distance is too small.

All the parallels are projected equal in length to the parallel 45°, namely, $2\pi r.\cos 45°$. The parallels between the equator and latitude 45° (both N. and S.) are therefore projected on a reduced scale; in *Fig. 14* it is as if the arc $C'E'D'$ has been 'compressed' into the straight line $C'RD'$. Polewards of latitude 45° the parallels are projected on an exaggerated scale.

On the globe, the length of the parallel in latitude ϕ is $2\pi r.\cos \phi$; on the projection, the length of this same parallel is $2\pi r.\cos 45°$. In order to determine the scale along the parallels it is thus sufficient to compare $\cos \phi$ and $\cos 45°$, as has been done in the following table for selected values of ϕ. The expression $\dfrac{\cos 45}{\cos \phi}$ gives the 'magnification factor' of the scale along the projected parallel in latitude ϕ:

$\phi°$	$\cos 45°$	$\cos \phi$	$\dfrac{\cos 45°}{\cos \phi}$	$\phi°$	$\cos 45°$	$\cos \phi$	$\dfrac{\cos 45°}{\cos \phi}$
90	0·7071	0·0000	∞	40	0·7071	0·7660	0·923
80		0·1736	4·074	30		0·8660	0·817
70		0·3420	2·067	20		0·9397	0·753
60		0·5000	1·414	10		0·9848	0·718
50		0·6428	1·100	0		1·0000	0·707

A comparison of this table with that given above in connexion with meridian scales is sufficient to reveal that, in polar latitudes, the exaggeration in scale is much greater along the parallels than along the meridians; for this reason the polar regions appear to be unduly 'crushed'. In spite of this somewhat glaring defect the projection is widely used for general maps of the whole globe, and for this purpose it is usually quite serviceable.

The complete projection is shown in *Fig. 15.*

Summary of Properties. The whole globe can be represented on one map in a form which makes an undoubted appeal to the popular mind. The scale along the parallels in latitude 45° (N. and S.) is correct; between the equator and latitude 45° the scale along the parallels is too small; polewards of latitude 45° the scale along the parallels is too great. The scale along the meridians is correct only in the immediate vicinity of the parallels in

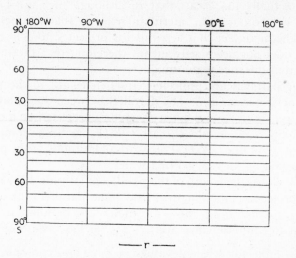

FIG. 15

GALL'S CYLINDRICAL PROJECTION

Parallels of latitude at intervals of 10°.

latitude 45° (N. and S.); between the equator and latitude 45° the meridian scale is too small; polewards of latitude 45° the meridian scale is too large. Without attempting to represent any single property with consistent accuracy over the entire map, the projection does achieve a fair measure of 'general compromise'.

Limitations. Away from the 'standard' parallels (45° N. and S.) the scale becomes inaccurate, varying from one latitude to another. In general, the scale along the parallels is not equal to the scale along the meridians, with the result that there is deformation of shape, especially in the polar regions. Between the equator and latitude 45° the scale along both meridians and parallels is too small; hence areas are projected too small. Polewards of 45° the scale along both meridians and parallels is too large; hence projected areas are too large.

Construction. The 'standard' parallels (45° N. and S.) are drawn
as parallel straight lines, $2\pi r.\cos 45°$ units long, and $2r.\cos 45°$
units apart; the lengths of all parallels are thereby determined,
for they are equal. The equator lies midway between the two
'standard' parallels. The projected parallel in latitude ϕ lies at a
distance of $\dfrac{r.\sin \phi \,(1+\cos 45°)}{1+\cos \phi}$ from the equator; any selected
parallel can therefore be drawn. The meridians are uniformly
spaced along the parallels; the distance on the projection between
the meridians θ' and θ'' is therefore $\dfrac{\theta'-\theta''}{360}.2\pi r.\cos 45°$.

<h3 style="text-align:center">MERCATOR'S PROJECTION</h3>

This is unquestionably one of the most renowned and familiar
of all map projections, and one which is widely used for world
maps, sometimes when it is not even really suitable. It has been
claimed that the 'popularity' of *Mercator's Projection* in Britain is
largely due to the fact that the 'British Empire' looks so much
larger in proportion to the rest of the world than it really is.
Without ascribing any 'imperialistic motive' to those who have
been responsible for the use of this projection for general world
maps, it is nevertheless almost certainly the case that there are
many people to-day who still regard *Mercator's* as the only 'true'
map; for them, any other map is a distorted and meaningless
hieroglyphic.

The underlying principle is briefly as follows. All parallels of
latitude are projected equal in length to the equator of the
'generating' globe, namely, $2\pi r$. The scale along the equator is
therefore true, but away from the equator the scale along the
parallels is exaggerated. The true length of the parallel in latitude
ϕ is $2\pi r.\cos \phi$; the projected length of this same parallel is $2\pi r$.
The 'magnification factor' of the scale along the parallels is thus
$\dfrac{2\pi r}{2\pi r.\cos \phi}$, or *sec* ϕ; that is, every parallel is projected *sec* ϕ times
its true length. The distances of the parallels from the equator
are then adjusted so as to make the scale along the meridians
at any point equal to the scale along the parallels at the *same point*.
In other words, the inevitable east-west 'stretching' is accompanied
by an *equal* north-south 'stretching' at every point over the entire
projection; but the actual amount of 'stretching' will clearly vary
from one latitude to another.

Thus, at every point, the representation of *shape* is true; but a different *scale* is required for each parallel of latitude. It is in respect of the correct representation of shape at any *point* that *Mercator's Projection* is said to be *orthomorphic*; in practice, the property of correct representation of shape can be extended to small areas (see also pp. 11 and 104).

Orthomorphism, however, is a property which requires careful interpretation when large areas are under consideration. Thus, a *small* square on the equator of the globe will be projected as a square; an *equally small* square in latitude 60° (N. or S.) will also be projected as a square, but as a square on a very *different scale*. In latitude 60° the parallel is projected at twice its true length (sec 60° = 2), and the sides of the small square are accordingly 'stretched' to twice their true length, while areas are 'stretched' to four times their true area. In latitude $75\frac{1}{2}$° (N. or S.) the linear scale is 'magnified' about four times; the poles, of course, cannot be projected, for the 'magnification factor' is infinite. Provided the areas under consideration are small, however, *shape* is accurately projected over the entire map. In the case of large areas, on the other hand, the limitation of *orthomorphism* is at once apparent, for there is ever present the difficulty of a changing scale over a continuous surface. It is instructive, for example, to compare Greenland with South America, both on the globe and on *Mercator's Projection*; actually, South America is about ten times the size of Greenland, but on the projection, Greenland appears to be rather the larger. Further, because Greenland lies wholly to the north of latitude 60°N., that is, in a region where the amount of 'stretching' is becoming rapidly more and more exaggerated, the *shape of the country as a whole* is very distorted on the projection; in the more northerly parts the exaggeration in the linear scale is four or five times as great as in the more southerly parts. South America, because it lies mainly within the tropics, where the amount of 'stretching' is so much less, possesses a very reasonable shape on the projection.

In spite of the disadvantages introduced by the exaggeration in scale away from the equator, *Mercator's Projection* will always be of value because it possesses one very important property, namely, that a straight line on the projection is a line of constant bearing, or *rhumb-line*. In view of the importance of constant bearing in navigation, *Mercator's Projection* is widely used for navigational purposes, both over the sea and in the air. In this connexion, however, it must be noted that great circles are not, in general, projected as straight lines. Consequently, it is usual to break up the great circle routes, which are the shortest possible over the surface of the globe, into a number of sections, throughout each of which it is possible to maintain constant bearing; a change of bearing is then necessary when leaving one section for the

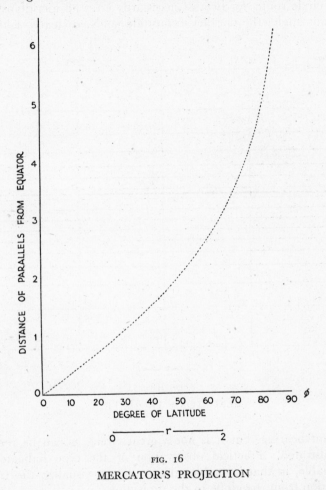

FIG. 16

MERCATOR'S PROJECTION

next. In this way a succession of constant-bearing straight lines is made to approximate to the projected great-circle curve.

The reader will find it most instructive if he carries out a few simple tests on the globe, and then compares his observations with the corresponding representation on the projection. Thus, a piece of thread, held taut between two points on the globe, indicates the great circle between those points; such a course can be accurately traced on the projection, where, in general, it will appear as a curve. (The equator and all meridians are the only great circles which are projected as straight lines.) A line of constant bearing on the globe will, in general, deviate from the great circle route, for it must necessarily cross all meridians at a constant angle; the parallel in latitude 50°N. is clearly a line of

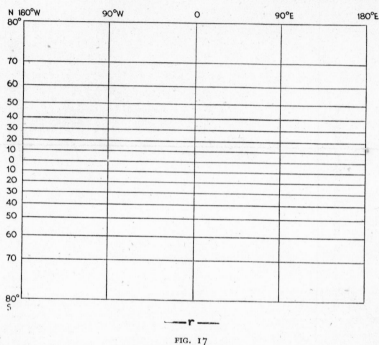

FIG. 17

MERCATOR'S PROJECTION

constant bearing, but it is not a great circle, as can be readily demonstrated. Practical observation of the type indicated is invaluable, in that it enables the reader to visualize the transformation from the globe to the projection.

The calculation of the spacing of the parallels is not easy to understand unless the reader is familiar with the calculus; but the distance (y) of the parallel in latitude ϕ from the equator is given by the equation: $y = r.\log_e \tan (45 + \frac{\phi}{2})$. This relationship is shown graphically in *Fig. 16*, in which the distance of the parallels from the equator is plotted against the angle of latitude.

The complete projection, to latitude 80°N. and S., is shown in *Fig. 17.* The poles obviously cannot be projected, for infinite 'magnification' of scale is entailed, which can only be effected at an infinite distance. Moreover, in the vicinity of the poles the exaggeration in the scales assumes excessive proportions; in latitude 87°N. and S., for example, linear dimensions are projected at about twenty times their true value, with the result that areas are 'magnified' about four hundred times.

Summary of Properties. All parallels of latitude are projected equal in length to the equator of the 'generating' globe. The spacing of the parallels is then adjusted so as to make the scale along the meridian at any particular point equal to the scale along the parallel at that point. As all meridians intersect all parallels at right angles, this adjustment of scale serves to make the projection *orthomorphic.* Thus, the shape of small areas is sensibly correct. A straight line on the projection is a line of constant bearing; hence *Mercator's Projection* is invaluable for navigational purposes.

Limitations. Along the equator the scale is correct, but away from the equator there is marked exaggeration; in latitude ϕ the 'magnification factor' is *sec* ϕ. Since exaggeration of the scale along the parallels is accompanied by equal exaggeration of the scale along the meridians, areas become grossly exaggerated in high latitudes. For this reason the polar regions cannot be satisfactorily projected.

Construction. The equator is drawn as a straight line, $2\pi r$ units long. The meridians are uniformly spaced, and drawn at right angles to the equator; the distance on the projection between the meridians θ' and θ'' is therefore $\dfrac{\theta' - \theta''}{360}.2\pi r$. The distance (y) of the parallel ϕ from the equator is given by the equation:

$$y = r.\log_e \tan \left(45 + \frac{\phi}{2}\right).$$

MERCATOR'S (TRANSVERSE) PROJECTION

If the projection is made *transverse,* that is, if the cylinder is regarded as touching the globe along the great circle formed by two selected opposite meridians, an excellent orthomorphic map can be made of an area which has only a small extent in longitude. Such a projection is, in fact, used for certain maps of the Ordnance Survey; for example, the Fifth (Relief) Edition, on a scale of one inch to one mile. Over a relatively small area such as Britain, the exaggeration in the scale away from the 'central' meridian is not very marked, whereas, for many purposes, *orthomorphism* is of prime importance. Moreover, although meridians and parallels are no longer, in general, straight lines, they do not deviate markedly from straight lines in the case of an area such as Britain, provided the 'central' meridian is carefully chosen; at the same time, the intersections of the meridians with the parallels are rectangular. Thus, scale, shape, area, and bearing are all projected with very little, if any, distortion, and an almost perfect map results.

LAMBERT'S CYLINDRICAL EQUAL-AREA PROJECTION

One method of applying the *equal-area* principle to a map of the whole globe is illustrated in *Fig. 18*. Let *ABCD* be a cylinder

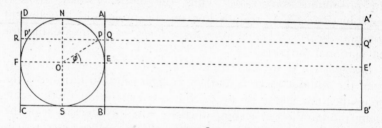

FIG. 18

LAMBERT'S CYLINDRICAL EQUAL-AREA PROJECTION

which touches the globe along the equator, and let *P* be a point on the surface of the globe in latitude ϕ. Let *EF* represent the plane of the equator, and let *QR* represent a parallel plane through *P*. Then the area on the surface of the globe, intercepted by these two planes, is equal to the area on the surface of the cylinder, intercepted by the same two planes. Therefore, if the cylinder be opened out to form the rectangle *AA'B'B*, the rectangle *QEE'Q'* will be equal in area to the surface zone on the globe, intercepted by the planes *EF* and *QR*.

The complete projection is shown in *Fig. 19*. It will be noticed that all parallels are projected equal in length to the equator; the parallel in latitude ϕ is therefore 'magnified' *sec* ϕ times. The *equal-area* property is achieved by balancing the inevitable east-west 'stretching' with an appropriate north-south 'compression'. In the polar regions, where the amount of east-west 'stretching' is considerable, the amount of north-south 'compression' is considerable also, with the result that *shape* is badly distorted. For this reason the projection is not widely used for maps of the whole globe; but for purely tropical regions, where there is only slight east-west 'stretching', and consequently only slight north-south 'compression', shape is not greatly distorted, and the projection is generally satisfactory for showing *equal-area* properties.

Summary of Properties. The parallels of latitude are all projected equal in length to the equator; the 'magnification factor' of the scale along the projected parallel ϕ is therefore *sec ϕ*. The spacing of the parallels is such that the *equal-area* property is preserved

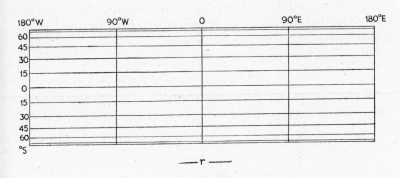

FIG. 19
LAMBERT'S CYLINDRICAL EQUAL-AREA PROJECTION
Parallels of latitude at intervals of 15°.

over the entire projection. The intersections of meridians with parallels are rectangular.

Limitations. The scale along the equator is correct, but away from the equator the scale along the parallels becomes increasingly exaggerated; at the same time, the scale along the meridians becomes progressively diminished. The marked inequality between the scale along the parallels, and the scale along the meridians, leads to pronounced deformation of shape in high latitudes; in the polar regions, for example, the projection is really of very little use.

Construction. The equator is drawn as a straight line, $2\pi r$ units long. The meridians are uniformly spaced, and drawn at right angles to the equator. The distance of the parallel in latitude ϕ from the equator is $r.\sin \phi$; alternatively, the spacing of the parallels may be determined graphically, as indicated in *Fig. 18* ($\angle POE$ is made equal to the required angle of latitude, and PQQ' is then drawn parallel to the equator EE').

CHAPTER IV

CONICAL PROJECTIONS

PROJECTIONS of this class can be visualized as made on a cone, which is afterwards opened out flat. In the *normal* position the axis of the cone is coincident with the axis of the 'generating' globe, but the cone may be regarded as either touching or cutting the globe, according to particular requirements. As in the case of the zenithal and cylindrical projections, both perspective and non-perspective projections are possible.

THE PERSPECTIVE CONICAL PROJECTION

In *Fig. 20*, which represents a section through the centre of the globe, at right angles to the plane of the equator, the cone

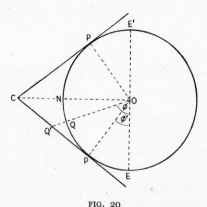

FIG. 20

PERSPECTIVE CONICAL PROJECTION

is shown touching the globe along the parallel in latitude ϕ'; that is, $\angle EOP = \phi'$. Let Q be a point on the surface of the globe in latitude ϕ ($\angle EOQ = \phi$), and let Q' be its projection on the cone when the point of origin is at the centre of the globe.

Then $\angle OCP = \angle EOP = \phi'$; $\angle POQ' = (\angle EOQ - \angle EOP) = (\phi - \phi')$; and $CP = r.\cot \phi'$.

When the cone is developed, that is, opened out flat, the parallel ϕ' will therefore be projected as the arc of a circle, the radius of which is $r.\cot \phi'$, and at its true length, namely, $2\pi r.\cos \phi'$.

44

Further, the apical angle of the developed cone will be $\dfrac{2\pi r.\cos\,\phi'}{r.\cot\,\phi'}$,

or $2\pi.\sin\,\phi'$ (in circular measure), which equals $\sin\,\phi'\times 360°$. The apical angle of the developed cone thus depends only on the latitude (ϕ') of the parallel of contact; for this reason the expression $\sin\,\phi'$ is often referred to as the *constant of the cone.*

The meridians will clearly be projected as straight lines, radiating from the apex of the developed cone at uniform angular intervals. The actual angle between any two given meridians on the projection will be the product of the angle between those same meridians on the globe into the constant of the cone; thus, if the selected meridians are spaced at intervals of $15°$ on the globe, these meridians will radiate from the apex of the developed cone at angular intervals of $\sin\,\phi'\times 15°$.

The parallels of latitude will be projected as concentric arcs of circles, described about the apex of the developed cone, and the distance (y) of the parallel ϕ from the *standard parallel* ϕ' is given by the relation $y=r.\tan\,(\phi-\phi')$. [In *Fig. 20*, $PQ'=OP.\tan\,\angle POQ'$ $=r.\tan\,(\angle EOQ'-\angle EOP)=r.\tan\,(\phi-\phi')$].

The projection of a complete hemisphere is shown in *Fig. 21*; in (*a*) the standard parallel is in latitude $45°$N.; in (*b*) the standard parallel is in latitude $30°$N.

The scale along the standard parallel is correct; along the other parallels the scale is exaggerated. On the standard parallel the meridian scale is also correct, but away from the standard parallel the meridian scale becomes increasingly exaggerated.

The true distance of the parallel ϕ from the standard parallel ϕ' is $r.(\phi-\phi')^{c}$; this distance is represented on the projection by $r.\tan\,(\phi-\phi')$. The following tables show the relation between $(\phi-\phi')^{c}$ and $\tan\,(\phi-\phi')$ for selected values of ϕ between $0°$ and $90°$, both when $\phi'=45°$, and when $\phi'=30°$:

$\phi'=45°$			$\phi'=30°$		
$\phi°$	$\tan\,(\phi-45)°$	$(\phi-45)^{c}$	$\phi°$	$\tan\,(\phi-30)°$	$(\phi-30)^{c}$
90	1·0000	0·7854	90	1·7321	1·0472
75	0·5774	0·5236	75	1·0000	0·7854
60	0·2679	0·2618	60	0·5774	0·5236
45	0·0000	0·0000	45	0·2679	0·2618
30	0·2679	0·2618	30	0·0000	0·0000
15	0·5774	0·5236	15	0·2679	0·2618
0	1·0000	0·7854	0	0·5774	0·5236

In order to obtain an indication of the scale along the meridians it is necessary to resort to a process of subtraction, as follows:

$\phi'=45°$	Differences		$\phi'=30°$	Differences	
$\phi°$	tan $(\phi-45)°$	$(\phi-45)^c$	$\phi°$	tan $(\phi-30)°$	$(\phi-30)^c$
90–75	0·4226	0·2618	90–75	0·7321	0·2618
75–60	0·3095	0·2618	75–60	0·4226	0·2618
60–45	0·2679	0·2618	60–45	0·3095	0·2618
45–30	0·2679	0·2618	45–30	0·2679	0·2618
30–15	0·3095	0·2618	30–15	0·2679	0·2618
15– 0	0·4226	0·2618	15– 0	0·3095	0·2618

Quite clearly, the scale along the meridians becomes increasingly exaggerated away from the standard parallel.

The pole of the globe is projected at the apex of the developed cone, which is the centre of the concentric arcs representing the parallels of latitude.

The radius of the arc of the projected parallel in latitude ϕ is CQ' (*Fig. 20*), that is, $(CP-Q'P)$, or $r.\cot \phi'-r.\tan (\phi-\phi')$. The length of the parallel is therefore $2\pi r.\sin \phi' [\cot \phi'- \tan (\phi-\phi')]$; but the length of this same parallel on the globe is $2\pi r.\cos \phi$. Let the expression $\sin \phi'[\cot \phi'-\tan (\phi-\phi')]$ be denoted by z; to compare the scale along the projected parallel ϕ with that of the globe, it is thus only necessary to show the relation between z and $\cos \phi$, as has been done in the following tables for selected values of ϕ, both when ϕ' is equal to 45°, and when ϕ' is equal to 30°:

$\phi'=45°$			$\phi'=30°$		
$\phi°$	z	$\cos \phi$	$\phi°$	z	$\cos \phi$
90	0·0000	0·0000	90	0·0000	0·0000
75	0·2988	0·2588	75	0·3660	0·2588
60	0·5177	0·5000	60	0·5773	0·5000
45	0·7071	0·7071	45	0·7321	0·7071
30	0·8965	0·8660	30	0·8660	0·8660
15	1·1115	0·9659	15	1·0000	0·9659
0	1·4142	1·0000	0	1·1547	1·0000

This perspective conical projection is of little practical value, for the zone of reasonable accuracy is a minimum, and there is really nothing to compensate for the gross inaccuracy away from the standard parallel; it does, however, serve to illustrate the basic principles underlying conical projection.

Summary of Properties. The scale along the standard parallel is correct; elsewhere the scale along the parallels is exaggerated, the exaggeration increasing markedly away from the standard parallel. The scale along the meridians is correct only at the standard parallel; elsewhere there is exaggeration, which increases

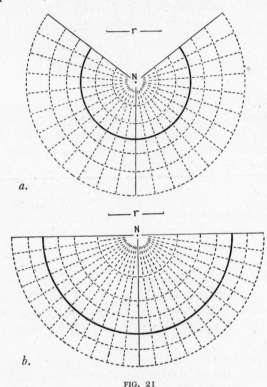

FIG. 21

PERSPECTIVE CONICAL PROJECTIONS

Meridians and parallels at intervals of 15°.

(*a*) Standard parallel in latitude 45° N.
(*b*) Standard parallel in latitude 30° N.

away from the standard parallel. Strictly correct representation is thus confined to a single line, namely, the standard parallel.

Limitations. Away from the standard parallel, the scale, along both the meridians and the parallels, becomes increasingly exaggerated; as a result, shape becomes very distorted. As there is no distinctive property inherent in the construction, there is nothing to compensate for the pronounced exaggeration in scale, and the projection is accordingly of little practical value.

Construction. With centre N, the projection of the North Pole, describe an arc of a circle of radius $r.\cot \phi'$, where ϕ' is the angle of latitude of the selected standard parallel, and r is the radius of the 'generating' globe. The apical angle of the developed cone is $\sin \phi' \times 360°$; within the angle thus marked out, the meridians radiate from N at uniform angular intervals. The distance of the parallel ϕ from the standard parallel ϕ' is $r.\tan (\phi - \phi')$.

THE SIMPLE CONICAL PROJECTION
(THE SIMPLE CONIC)

The *Simple Conic*, as generally understood, is a non-perspective conical projection, based on *one standard parallel*; that is, the cone may be regarded as touching the 'generating' globe along one selected parallel of latitude. In *Fig. 20*, the cone is shown touching the globe along the parallel ϕ'; this is the *standard parallel*, which is projected as the arc of a circle of radius $r.\cot \phi'$, and at its true length, $2\pi r.\cos \phi'$. Thus, the projected arc representing the standard parallel subtends at the apex of the developed cone an angle $\sin \phi' \times 360°$. All other parallels are projected as concentric arcs of circles, spaced at their true distances from the standard parallel. The meridians are projected as radii from the apex of the developed cone; but the apex is not now the projection of the pole, which is, in general, represented by an arc of a circle. The projection of a complete hemisphere is shown in *Fig. 22*; in (*a*) the standard parallel is in latitude 45° N.; in (*b*) the standard parallel is in latitude 30° N.

The scale is correct along the standard parallel and along all meridians; since the projected parallels are concentric circular arcs, and since the projected meridians are everywhere radial to these arcs, it follows that the distance between any two given parallels is the same along all meridians, and hence that the meridian scale is everywhere correct. Purely with reference to distances measured along the meridians, this projection may therefore be styled 'equidistant'.

The radius of the projected parallel in latitude ϕ' is $r.\cot \phi'$, and the radius of the parallel in latitude ϕ is therefore $r[\cot \phi' - (\phi - \phi')^c]$. The length of the projected parallel ϕ is therefore $2\pi r.\sin \phi'[\cot \phi' - (\phi - \phi')^c]$; the length of this same parallel on the globe is $2\pi r.\cos \phi$. Let the expression $\sin \phi'[\cot \phi' - (\phi - \phi')^c]$ be denoted by ζ. To compare the scale along the projected parallel ϕ with that of the globe, it is therefore

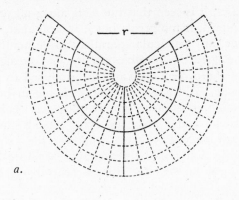

a.

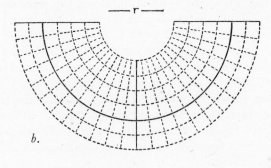

b.

FIG. 22

SIMPLE CONICAL PROJECTION WITH ONE STANDARD
PARALLEL (THE SIMPLE CONIC)

Meridians and parallels at intervals of 15°.

(*a*) Standard parallel in latitude 45° N.
(*b*) Standard parallel in latitude 30° N.

only necessary to show the relation between z and cos ϕ, as has
been done in the following tables for selected values of ϕ, both
when ϕ' is equal to 45°, and when ϕ' is equal to 30°:

$\phi°$	$\phi'=45°$ z	cos ϕ	$\phi°$	$\phi'=30°$ z	cos ϕ
90	0·1517	0·0000	90	0·3425	0·0000
75	0·3369	0·2588	75	0·4734	0·2588
60	0·5220	0·5000	60	0·6042	0·5000
45	0·7071	0·7071	45	0·7351	0·7071
30	0·8922	0·8660	30	0·8660	0·8660
15	1·0773	0·9659	15	0·9969	0·9659
0	1·2625	1·0000	0	1·1278	1·0000

4

In both cases, it is seen that the scale along all parallels, other than the standard, is too great; but it is clear that, by a suitable choice of cone, any particular parallel can be made *standard*. In this way the greatest possible accuracy, consistent with the limitations of the projection, can be introduced to any specified latitudinal zone. Although extremely simple in both principle and construction, this projection is quite serviceable for many purposes, provided the area surveyed extends through a few degrees of latitude only. Then, whatever the extent in longitude, the projection will be reasonably accurate, for no part of the area need be very far from a centrally-placed standard parallel.

Summary of Properties. The scale along the standard parallel, and along all meridians, is true to the globe from which the projection has been developed; but the scale along all other parallels becomes increasingly exaggerated away from the standard parallel. Thus, for a narrow belt along the standard parallel the representation is satisfactory for most purposes.

Limitations. Away from the standard parallel the scale along the parallels increases somewhat rapidly; and, since the scale along the meridians remains true, shape becomes very distorted. The projection is not suitable for an area which covers more than a few degrees of latitude.

Construction. The standard parallel (ϕ') is drawn as an arc of a circle of radius $r.\cot \phi'$; and of correct length, namely, $2\pi r.\cos \phi'$; thus, the projected arc subtends at the apex (N) of the developed cone an angle of $\sin \phi' \times 360°$. The meridians are drawn as radii from N, spaced at uniform angular intervals; thus, the angle between the projected meridians $\theta°$ and $(\theta+1)°$ is $\sin \phi'°$. The distance of the projected parallel ϕ from the standard parallel ϕ' is $\dfrac{(\phi-\phi').2\pi r}{360}$; the parallels are drawn as concentric arcs, and are limited by the radial (straight-line) meridians drawn to the standard parallel. Since the spacing of the parallels is determined with reference to the standard parallel, the pole is projected as the arc of a circle drawn through points which, when measured along each meridian, are at a distance of $\dfrac{(90-\phi').2\pi r}{360}$ from the standard parallel.

THE ONE-STANDARD EQUAL-AREA CONICAL PROJECTION

As its name implies, this is a non-perspective conical projection, based on one standard parallel, and modified so that *areas* are everywhere correctly represented.

The standard parallel (ϕ') is projected as the arc of a circle of radius $r.\cot \phi'$, and at its correct length, namely, $2\pi r.\cos \phi'$. The meridians are then drawn as radii from the apex of the developed cone to intersect the standard parallel at uniform intervals; that is, the scale along the standard parallel is everywhere true. All parallels of latitude are drawn as arcs of concentric circles about the apex of the developed cone, but the distances of the arcs from the standard parallel are adjusted so as to preserve the property of *equal-area*.

On the globe, the area of the zone from the pole to the parallel ϕ is $2\pi r^2(1 - \sin \phi)$; and the area between the parallels ϕ and ϕ' is therefore $2\pi r^2(\sin \phi - \sin \phi')$. Let R be the radius of the pro-jected parallel in latitude ϕ. Then the area on the projection, from the apex of the developed cone to the parallel ϕ, is $\sin \phi'.\pi R^2$ (where $\sin \phi'$ is the constant of the cone). The area on the projection between the parallels ϕ and ϕ' is therefore $\pi.\sin \phi'.(R^2 - r^2\cot^2\phi')$. Thus, if the *area* is to be projected true to the scale of the globe, $\pi.\sin \phi'(R^2 - r^2\cot^2\phi') = 2\pi r^2(\sin \phi - \sin \phi')$

whence $R^2 = r^2 \dfrac{(\sin \phi'.\cot^2\phi' + 2 \sin \phi - 2 \sin \phi')}{\sin \phi'}$.

Hence, for any given value of ϕ', that is, for any given stan-dard parallel, the value of R for selected parallels (ϕ) can be determined.

The projection of a complete hemisphere is shown in *Fig. 23*; in (*a*) the standard parallel is in latitude 45°N.; in (*b*) the standard parallel is in latitude 30°N.

The scale along the standard parallel is everywhere correct; along the other parallels there is exaggeration of the scale, and the exaggeration increases away from the standard parallel. At the standard parallel the scale along the meridians is correct; away from the standard parallel the scale along the meridians is progressively diminished. East-west 'stretching' is thus com-pensated by north-south 'compression', and so the *equal-area* property is achieved.

Let R' be the radius of the projected parallel in latitude ϕ when the 'generating' globe is of unit radius; let D_p be the distance on

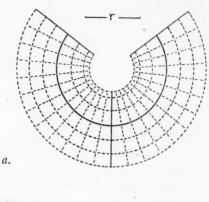

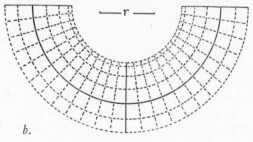

FIG. 23

EQUAL-AREA CONICAL PROJECTION WITH ONE STANDARD
PARALLEL

Meridians and parallels at intervals of 15°.

(a) Standard parallel in latitude 45° N.
(b) Standard parallel in latitude 30° N.

the projection of the parallel ϕ from the standard parallel ϕ'; and let D_g be the true distance between these same parallels. The following tables show the relation between D_p and D_g:

$\phi'=45°$				$\phi'=30°$			
$\phi°$	R'	D_p	D_g	$\phi°$	R'	D_p	D_g
90	0·414	0·586	0·785	90	1·000	0·732	1·047
75	0·518	0·482	0·524	75	1·066	0·666	0·785
60	0·742	0·258	0·262	60	1·238	0·494	0·524
45	1·000	0·000	0·000	45	1·474	0·258	0·262
30	1·259	0·259	0·262	30	1·732	0·000	0·000
15	1·506	0·506	0·524	15	1·991	0·259	0·262
0	1·732	0·732	0·785	0	2·236	0·504	0·524

The tables, as presented, give the spacing of selected parallels, but comparative indications of *scale* can be obtained by a process of subtraction, as follows:

$\phi'=45°$			$\phi'=30°$		
	Differences			Differences	
$\phi°$	D_p	D_g	$\phi°$	D_p	D_g
90–75	0·104	0·262	90–75	0·066	0·262
75–60	0·224	0·262	75–60	0·172	0·262
60–45	0·258	0·262	60–45	0·236	0·262
45–30	0·259	0·262	45–30	0·258	0·262
30–15	0·247	0·262	30–15	0·259	0·262
15– 0	0·226	0·262	15– 0	0·245	0·262

It is now clear that, in the vicinity of the standard parallel, the scale along the meridians is reasonably correct; away from the standard parallel, the scale along the meridians becomes progressively diminished.

The length of the projected parallel in latitude ϕ is $2\pi R.\sin\phi'$, where R is the radius of the projected parallel, and $\sin\phi'$ the constant of the cone; the true length of this same parallel is $2\pi r.\cos\phi$. To compare the scale along the projected parallel ϕ with that of the globe, it is only necessary to show the relation between $R.\sin\phi'$ and $\cos\phi$ (where R is evaluated for selected values of ϕ, as indicated above); $r=1$:

$\phi'=45°$			$\phi'=30°$		
$\phi°$	$R.\sin\phi'$	$\cos\phi$	$\phi°$	$R.\sin\phi'$	$\cos\phi$
90	0·293	0·000	90	0·500	0·000
75	0·366	0·259	75	0·533	0·259
60	0·525	0·500	60	0·619	0·500
45	0·707	0·707	45	0·737	0·707
30	0·890	0·866	30	0·866	0·866
15	1·065	0·966	15	0·995	0·966
0	1·225	1·000	0	1·118	1·000

The scale is correct, therefore, only along the standard parallel, but for a narrow belt near the standard parallel the representation of distance, along both the meridians and the parallels, is not unsatisfactory.

Summary of Properties. Although the actual scale is correct only along one line, namely, the standard parallel, *areas* are correctly represented over the entire projection. This *equal-area* property is achieved by balancing east-west 'stretching' with north-south 'compression'.

Limitations. Away from the standard parallel the scale along the parallels becomes progressively exaggerated; consequently the scale along the meridians becomes progressively diminished. Shape is therefore distorted away from the standard parallel.

Construction. The standard parallel (ϕ') is drawn as an arc of a circle of radius $r.\cot \phi'$, and of correct length, namely, $2\pi r.\cos \phi'$; thus the projected arc subtends at the apex (N) of the developed cone an angle of $\sin \phi' \times 360°$. The meridians are drawn as radii from N, spaced at uniform angular intervals; thus, the angle between the projected meridians $0°$ and $(\theta+1)°$ is $\sin \phi'^°$. The projected parallels are drawn as concentric circular arcs about N as centre; the radius R of the projected parallel in latitude ϕ is given by the relation: $R^2 = r^2\dfrac{(\sin \phi'.\cot^2\phi' + 2\sin \phi - 2\sin \phi')}{\sin \phi'}$.

THE TWO-STANDARD CONICAL PROJECTION

This non-perspective projection may be visualized as made on a cone which 'intersects' the globe along two selected parallels of latitude; these are the two *standard* parallels. On account of this apparent intersection of the globe, the projection is often referred to as the '*Secant Conic*'; but the name is very misleading, since it implies that the projected distance between the two standard parallels is made equal to the *secant distance* between them on the globe, whereas it is actually made equal to the *arc distance* on the surface of the globe.

In *Fig. 24*, let the two standard parallels be PP' (in latitude ϕ') and QQ' (in latitude ϕ''). These two parallels are projected as concentric arcs of circles about the apex of the developed cone, true to scale, and separated by the correct distance, after the manner of *Fig. 25*, which is not drawn to scale.

Thus, the arc $\qquad PP' = 2\pi r.\cos \phi'$;

the arc $\qquad QQ' = 2\pi r.\cos \phi''$;

the distance $\qquad PQ = 2\pi r.\left(\dfrac{\phi''-\phi'}{360}\right)$;

and O is the apex of the developed cone.

The two sectors, OPP' and OQQ', are clearly similar;

therefore $\dfrac{OP}{OQ} = \dfrac{\text{arc } PP'}{\text{arc } QQ'} = \dfrac{2\pi r.\cos \phi'}{2\pi r.\cos \phi''}$ .... (i)

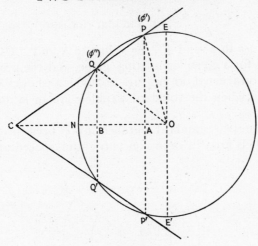

FIG. 24

CONICAL PROJECTION WITH TWO STANDARD PARALLELS

Let $OQ = R$; then $OP = R + 2\pi r . \left(\dfrac{\phi'' - \phi'}{360} \right)$;

and equation (i) becomes: $\dfrac{R + 2\pi r . \left(\dfrac{\phi'' - \phi'}{360} \right)}{R} = \dfrac{2\pi r . \cos \phi'}{2\pi r . \cos \phi''}$

whence $R = 2\pi r . \left(\dfrac{\phi'' - \phi'}{360} \right) . \left(\dfrac{\cos \phi''}{\cos \phi' - \cos \phi''} \right)$.

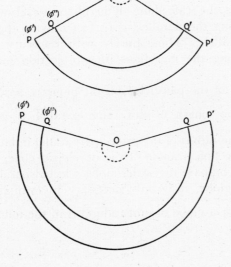

FIG. 25

(Not to scale.)

But $\angle QOQ' = \dfrac{2\pi r.\cos \phi''}{R}$ (in circular measure); so, by giving specific values to ϕ' and ϕ'', the values of R and $\angle QOQ'$ can be determined for a given 'generating' globe, and the projection can then be constructed as in *Fig. 26*, which shows a complete hemisphere, when the standard parallels are in latitudes 30°N. and 60°N.

When the two standard parallels have been projected, the other parallels are drawn as concentric arcs, spaced at their true

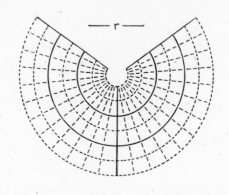

FIG. 26

CONICAL PROJECTION WITH TWO STANDARD PARALLELS

Meridians and parallels at intervals of 15°.
Standard parallels in latitudes 30° N and 60° N.

distances; thus, the scale along all meridians is everywhere correct. The scale along the parallels is correct only in the case of the standard parallels. Thus, purely with reference to distances measured along the meridians, this projection may be styled 'equidistant'.

The length of the parallel ϕ on the globe is $2\pi r.\cos \phi$; on the projection, the length of this same parallel is $2\pi R_\phi . \dfrac{\angle QOQ'}{360}$, where R_ϕ is the radius of the projected parallel in latitude ϕ, and $\angle QOQ'$ is the apical angle of the developed cone, expressed in degrees. To compare the scales along selected parallels with the scale of the globe, it is only necessary to evaluate $\cos \phi$ and $R_\phi . \dfrac{\angle QOQ'}{360}$ for a globe of unit radius, as in the following table:

Standard parallels: $\phi'=30°$, $\phi''=60°$

$\phi°$	$R_\phi . \dfrac{\angle QOQ'}{360}$	$\cos \phi$
90	0·134	0·000
75	0·317	0·259
60	0·500	0·500
45	0·679	0·707
30	0·866	0·866
15	1·049	0·966
0	1·232	1·000

It will be noticed that, *between* the two standard parallels, the scale along the parallels is too small; but that, *outside* the standard parallels, the scale along the parallels is too great. By making two parallels *standard*, however, there is a much better opportunity of extending the area within which the scale is reasonably accurate than is possible in the case of the *simple conic*. The choice of the standard parallels is quite arbitrary and a suitable choice depends entirely upon the area to be mapped and the purpose of the map. Thus, it might be desirable to give the best possible distribution of accuracy over the entire area surveyed; alternatively, it might be preferable to obtain much greater accuracy in one part of the projection than in another.

Although the scale is everywhere true along all meridians, the projection is not really suitable for an area which has a great extent in latitude, for then it is not possible to bring the standard parallels sufficiently close together to ensure reasonable accuracy along the other parallels. For a country such as Britain, which covers only about 10° of latitude, the projection is very satisfactory, and most atlases contain maps of Britain drawn on the *two-standard conic*. The projection is also satisfactory for belts of country which have an appreciable extent in longitude, but no great extent in latitude; for example, the course of the Canadian trans-continental railways, and the course of the Trans-Siberian Railway.

Summary of Properties. The scale along the two standard parallels, and along all meridians, is true; *between* the standard parallels, projected parallels are on a reduced scale; *outside* the standard parallels, projected parallels are on an exaggerated scale. By a careful choice of standard parallels, however, it is possible to obtain good representation over a fairly large area, provided the area has no very great extent in latitude.

Limitations. Since there is progressive distortion of scale along the parallels which lie at a distance from the standard parallels, it is important for good representation that the area mapped should not extend through many degrees of latitude. The scale along the meridians remains true, of course, throughout the entire range of latitude; but the scale along the parallels is strictly true only along the standard parallels, and reasonably true only in their immediate neighbourhood. If possible, therefore, no part of the area surveyed should be far removed from a standard parallel.

Construction. Let ϕ' and ϕ'' be the angles of latitude of the two standard parallels; and let ϕ'' be the higher latitude. Let O be the apex of the developed cone, and let R be the radius of the projected parallel ϕ'', which is described as an arc of a circle about O. Then $R = 2\pi r . \left(\dfrac{\phi'' - \phi'}{360}\right) . \left(\dfrac{\cos \phi''}{\cos \phi' - \cos \phi''}\right)$. The projected parallel ϕ'' subtends at O an angle of $\dfrac{2\pi r . \cos \phi''}{R}$ (in circular measure). To the arc thus delimited the meridians are drawn, radiating from O at uniform intervals. All other parallels are drawn as concentric arcs, at their true distances from the standard parallel ϕ''; thus the distance of the other standard parallel (ϕ') is $\dfrac{2\pi r . (\phi'' - \phi')}{360}$.

THE POLYCONIC PROJECTION

In this projection, every parallel of latitude is projected as if it were a *standard* parallel; that is, as the arc of a circle of radius $r.\cot \phi$, and at its true length, $2\pi r.\cos \phi$, where ϕ is the latitude of the parallel in question. In effect, therefore, each parallel is projected as if it were developed from its own particular cone; this feature gives point to the name.

In the case of the equator, the 'cone' becomes a cylinder, and the equator is thus projected as a straight line; in the case of the poles, the 'cone' becomes a plane, and the poles are thus projected as points.

The *central* meridian is projected as a straight line, perpendicular to the equator, and correctly divided for the points of intersection with selected parallels; in other words, the scale along the central meridian is everywhere correct. Thus, if ϕ' and ϕ'' are two selected parallels, the true distance between them is $\dfrac{(\phi' - \phi'').2\pi r}{360}$; this must also be the distance between them along the central meridian of the projection. Starting from any selected parallel, for example, the equator, the central meridian can be correctly divided for the spacing of the parallels, and the centres of the projected arcs can then be determined, for the centres all lie along the line of the central meridian, and the radius of each particular arc is known ($r.\cot\phi$). The *constant of the cone* ($\sin\phi$) for each selected parallel can then be used to determine graphically the length of arc; thus, the projected arc in latitude ϕ will subtend at the apex of the developed cone an angle of $\sin\phi \times 360°$.

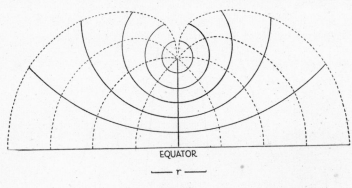

EQUATOR

—— r ——

FIG. 27

THE POLYCONIC

Parallels at intervals of 15°; meridians at intervals of 45°.

Each parallel is correctly divided for the points of intersection with selected meridians, which are then drawn as curves through corresponding points. The scale is thus true along every parallel of latitude and along the central meridian. Away from the central meridian, however, the meridian scale is exaggerated.

The projection of a complete hemisphere is shown in *Fig. 27*, in which the parallels are drawn at intervals of 15°, and the meridians at intervals of 45°.

This projection is clearly not very suitable for large areas, but it is widely used for topographical maps of small areas, although frequently with modifications. One such modification is to restrict the east-west extent of the area mapped with reference to any one central meridian. Thus, the whole region under survey is divided into narrow 'strips', the east-west extent of which is limited in conformity with the degree of accuracy required in the scale. Each strip is then mapped independently and with reference to its own particular *central* meridian. Since every parallel is projected as a *standard*, the curvature and scale of projected parallels are independent of the position of the central meridian. Hence, when a large map is cut up into a number of 'sheets', which are plotted with reference to their individual central meridians, adjacent north-south sheets will fit exactly; but since the boundary meridians of each sheet are curved, adjacent east-west sheets will have a 'rolling fit', as shown in *Fig. 28*. The great advantage of this particular modification is that, after the several *central* meridians have been selected, each sheet can then be

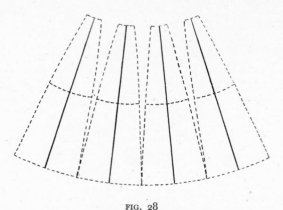

FIG. 28

THE POLYCONIC

The mapping of an area in 'sheets', by making use of a number of 'central' meridians.
(Not to scale.)

regarded as an entity, and can be mapped regardless of neighbouring sheets.

Summary of Properties. The scale along all parallels is true, for all are projected as *standard*, that is, as circular arcs of radius $r.\cot\phi$, and $2\pi r.\cos\phi$ in length. The scale along the central meridian is also true, but the scale along the other meridians increases rapidly away from the central meridian. The central meridian intersects all parallels at right angles; and, because both parallels and meridians are curved, there are no very oblique intersections of parallels with meridians. Near the central meridian, therefore, the representation is remarkably good, a feature which has been recognized by the frequent use of the projection for large-scale topographical maps.

Limitations. Although the scale along the parallels is everywhere true, the meridian scale is very variable from one part of the projection to another. The *polyconic* is therefore not really suitable for the mapping of large areas if continuity of projection is desired, for, away from the central meridian, marked distortion occurs. If, however, it is permissible to map the area in individual sheets, each plotted with reference to its own *central* meridian, the difficulty of a varying scale can be overcome; but the several sheets cannot be fitted together to make one continuous map, although a limited number can be made to fit together fairly well.

Construction. Project the selected parallel (ϕ') as an arc of a circle of radius $r.\cot \phi'$, described about some suitable point (O). The length of this projected parallel must be $2\pi r.\cos \phi'$; that is, the arc must subtend at O an angle of $\sin \phi' \times 360°$. Draw a straight line through O to intersect the projected parallel ϕ' at its mid-point (P); the line OP is then the central meridian, along which the scale must be everywhere true. Starting from P, it is therefore possible to mark off along the central meridian OP the correct spacing for other selected parallels; and, as the radii of these projected parallels are known, it is also possible to determine the positions of the centres of the circles of which the projected arcs form a part, for the centres all lie along OP. Each parallel must be projected at its true length; that is, the parallel ϕ subtends at its own particular 'centre' an angle of $\sin \phi \times 360°$. Each parallel is then correctly divided for the points of intersection with selected meridians, which are drawn as smooth curves through corresponding points on the different parallels.

THE 'INTERNATIONAL MAP'

This map, which is on a scale of 1 : 1,000,000 (usually written 1 : M), is drawn on a modified form of the *polyconic*. Each sheet of the map covers 4° of latitude and 6° of longitude; polewards of latitude 60°, however, the sheets cover 12° of longitude.

The meridian scale is made true along each of the meridians which lie 2° from the central meridian (polewards of latitude 60°, it is presumably intended that the necessary adjustment should be made to the meridians which lie 4° from the central meridian). The bounding parallels of each sheet are thus slightly closer together than in the case of the *polyconic*, where the scale is made true along the central meridian itself; but all parallels are still arcs of circles of radius $r.\cot \phi$.

Actually this adjustment, whereby the meridian scale is made true along two meridians instead of only one, is very small and is, for most practical purposes, negligible on the sheets. It is almost certainly less than the variations which might reasonably be expected to occur in the material of the map sheet as a result of varying atmospheric conditions. Theoretically, on the other hand, the idea is sound, in that it provides for a better distribution of accuracy.

A second modification concerns the meridians. The bounding parallels are correctly divided for the points of intersection with selected meridians, which are then drawn as *straight* lines joining corresponding points on the bounding parallels. This modification facilitates the joining of adjacent sheets along their eastern and western margins; the 'rolling fit' of the *polyconic* sheets, while not really inconvenient when only two or three sheets are concerned, is troublesome when several sheets have to be joined.

The method of dividing the meridians, other than the two 'standard' meridians, for the points of intersection with selected parallels, was not expressly defined by the original committee responsible for detail. It might reasonably be inferred that every meridian should be divided correctly, and that corresponding points be then joined by smooth curves; alternatively, arcs of circles of radius $r.\cot \phi$ could be drawn through the appropriate points on the 'standard' meridians. This, again, is a nicety which is of theoretical, rather than of practical, significance; in the main, the sheets cover relatively small areas, and the difference between the two methods is scarcely perceptible, and quite negligible on the actual sheets.

As in the case of the *polyconic*, since every parallel of latitude is projected as a *standard* parallel, any chosen area can be mapped independently of neighbouring areas, merely by selecting a convenient *central* meridian, and plotting with reference to that meridian. This is the principle of mapping on separate sheets, a feature which facilitates independent surveying and plotting. The sheets, although separate and 'complete' in themselves, form part of a uniform system.

Quite clearly, though, since the actual surveying and plotting must necessarily be undertaken by many different States, the quality of the resulting sheets is somewhat uneven, both on the grounds of accuracy, and in the beauty and clarity achieved.

BONNE'S PROJECTION

This is an example of a modified conical projection in which the idea of 'projection', as generally understood, is not very apparent. One selected parallel of latitude (ϕ') is drawn as if it were the standard parallel of the *simple conic*; that is, as an arc of a circle of radius $r.\cot \phi'$, and of length $2\pi r.\cos \phi'$. All other parallels are then drawn as *concentric* arcs, at their true length ($2\pi r.\cos \phi$), and correctly spaced along the central meridian. Each parallel is correctly divided for the points of intersection with selected meridians; that is, the scale along all parallels is everywhere true. The meridians are drawn as smooth curves through corresponding points on the different parallels; the central meridian is thus the only one along which the scale is everywhere true, for the meridians are not, in general, radial to the projected arcs which represent the parallels of latitude. The radial distance between two selected parallels is, of course, constant throughout their entire length, for the arcs are concentric; only the central meridian, however, is radial to all parallels.

The *central* meridian intersects all parallels at right angles; the *standard* parallel intersects all meridians at right angles. Elsewhere the intersections are oblique, the obliquity increasing diagonally away from the centre of the projection, thus producing gross distortion of shape, especially in the 'corners'.

The modifications embodied in the construction serve to make this an *equal-area* projection, and it is this property which contributes so much to the value of the projection.

Since every parallel is projected at its true length, and since the distance between selected parallels is true along the central meridian, and constant throughout their entire length, it follows that the area contained between two selected parallels on the projection is equal to the area between those same parallels on the globe. In the minds of some readers, however, uncertainty concerning the *equal-area* property may arise, for the radial distance between selected parallels is not, in general, measured along the meridians, which are oblique to the parallels, and hence in marked contrast to the condition on the globe; there may be, in fact, a tendency to confuse two issues, namely, *area* and *shape*. The following calculations should provide some measure of reassurance for those who tend to remain sceptical.

Let the radius of the 'generating' globe be r; let the *standard* parallel be in latitude ϕ', and let ϕ be the latitude of any other selected parallel. Then the length of the parallel ϕ, both on the projection and on the globe, is $2\pi r.\cos \phi$; the length of the parallel ($\phi+1$) is $2\pi r.\cos (\phi+1)$. The distance between these two parallels, both on the globe and along the central meridian on the projection, is $\dfrac{2\pi r}{360}$. The area between the two parallels on the projection may therefore be taken as:

$$\frac{2\pi r}{360}\cdot\tfrac{1}{2}[2\pi r.\cos\,(\phi+1)+2\pi r.\cos\,\phi]\ \text{(very nearly)}$$

that is, $\dfrac{\pi^2 r^2}{180}\,[\cos\,(\phi+1)+\cos\,\phi].$

But the area between these same two parallels on the globe is $2\pi r^2[\sin\,(\phi+1)-\sin\,\phi]$. The following table gives the values of the area between the parallels ϕ and $(\phi+1)$, on the globe and on the projection, when r is equal to 1:

ϕ°	Area (globe)	Area (projection)
0	0·1097	0·1097
15	0·1057	0·1057
30	0·0945	0·0945
45	0·0768	0·0768
60	0·0540	0·0540
75	0·0275	0·0275

The *equal-area* property is thus maintained, but at the expense of *shape*, except along the *central* meridian and the *standard* parallel, where the intersections are rectangular. Away from the central meridian and the standard parallel, distortion of shape is inevitable, and a small square on the globe is projected as an *equal-area* parallelogram, in which the scale along one pair of opposite sides (the parallels) is true, while the scale along the other pair (the meridians) is exaggerated. Moreover, the meridian scale varies considerably from one part of the projection to another, for the obliquity of the intersections varies.

Provided the *standard* parallel and the *central* meridian are carefully chosen, *Bonne's Projection* is very serviceable for compact areas such as, for example, France; and it has been used with success for large-scale topographical maps of certain European countries. In such cases it is possible to choose the central meridian and standard parallel so that no part of the area is far from both these 'true' lines. Large areas such as Asia are frequently mapped on this projection, but the distortion of shape then becomes conspicuous, and for this reason the *oblique zenithal equal-area projection* is sometimes preferred (see p. 99).

The projection of a complete hemisphere is shown in *Fig. 29*.

Summary of Properties. The scale along all parallels and the central meridian is true; along other meridians there is exaggeration, which increases away from the central meridian. The *equal-area* property is preserved over the entire projection. The intersections of the central meridian with all parallels, and of the standard parallel with all meridians, are rectangular; along two narrow zones, therefore, reasonably correct representation of shape is combined with *equal-area*.

Limitations. Away from the central meridian, the scale along the meridians increases rapidly, and shape becomes grossly distorted, especially in the 'corners'. Although the *equal-area* property applies to the entire projection, distortion of shape and meridian scale limit the size of areas which can be satisfactorily mapped.

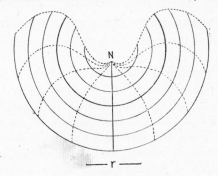

FIG. 29

BONNE'S PROJECTION

'*Standard*' parallel in latitude 45° N. Parallels at intervals of 15°; meridians at intervals of 45°.

Construction. The *standard* parallel (ϕ') is projected as an arc of a circle of radius $r.\cot \phi'$, and at its true length, namely, $2\pi r.\cos \phi'$; that is, it subtends at the centre, about which the arc is described, an angle of $\sin \phi' \times 360°$. The *central* meridian is drawn radially to the standard parallel, through the mid-point of the parallel. The central meridian is divided correctly for the spacing of selected parallels, which are then drawn as concentric arcs of circles, and all at their true length. Since the true length of each parallel is known, and since the radius of each projected arc is also known, the angle subtended by the concentric arcs at their common centre can be determined; in this way the arcs can be projected at their true lengths. All parallels are correctly divided for the points of intersection with selected meridians; this, again, can be done by making use of the fact that equal arcs subtend equal angles at the centre of the circle. The other meridians are drawn as smooth curves through corresponding points on the parallels.

5

CHAPTER V

CONVENTIONAL PROJECTIONS

PROJECTIONS of this class are best regarded as mathematical devices, designed for some specific purpose. They are not 'projected' in the usual sense of the word; nor are they, in general, modified from perspective prototypes; and even where such modification has been effected, it is not always readily apparent.

SANSON-FLAMSTEED'S (SINUSOIDAL) PROJECTION

Mathematically, the *sinusoidal projection* is a particular case of *Bonne's*, designed to show the whole globe on one map.

The *standard* parallel is the equator, which is projected as a straight line, at its true length, and correctly divided for the points of intersection with selected meridians. (In *Bonne's Projection*, the standard parallel (ϕ') is drawn as an arc of a circle of radius $r.\cot \phi'$; hence, when the standard parallel is the equator, and $\phi' = 0°$, $\cot \phi'$ becomes infinite, and the projected parallel therefore becomes an arc of infinite radius, that is, a straight line.)

The *central* meridian is also a straight line, perpendicular to, and equal to one-half the length of, the equator; this meridian is correctly divided for the spacing of selected parallels.

The parallels are all straight lines, parallel to the equator, and of correct length, namely, $2\pi r.\cos \phi$, where ϕ is the latitude. (In *Bonne's Projection*, the projected parallels are all concentric arcs, that is, 'parallel' to the standard.) All the parallels are correctly divided for the points of intersection with selected meridians, which are then drawn as smooth curves through corresponding points. The projected meridians are actually *sine* curves, a feature of the projection which gives point to the name '*sinusoidal*'.

As in the case of *Bonne's Projection*, *area* is correctly represented; but when the whole globe is shown on one map, *shape* becomes very distorted diagonally away from the centre, and it is on account of this failing that the usefulness of the projection for world maps is restricted.

The scale along the central meridian and all parallels is true; but in the case of other meridians there is considerable variation from one part of the projection to another, as a result of the varying obliquity of the intersections of meridians with parallels.

In any given latitude (ϕ), however, the scale along a meridian (θ) can be determined approximately as follows:

The distance from the central meridian to the point of intersection of the meridian θ with the parallel $(\phi-1)$ is $\dfrac{\theta}{180}\pi r.\cos(\phi-1)$; the distance from the central meridian to the point of intersection of the meridian θ with the parallel $(\phi+1)$ is $\dfrac{\theta}{180}\pi r.\cos(\phi+1)$.

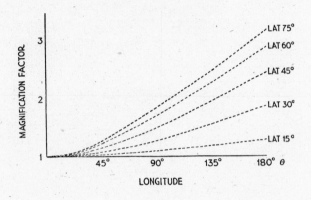

FIG. 30

SANSON-FLAMSTEED'S (SINUSOIDAL) PROJECTION

Graph to show the relation between the meridian scale and the longitude, in selected latitudes.

Let the difference between these two distances be d'. The perpendicular distance between the two projected parallels $(\phi+1)$ and $(\phi-1)$ is $\dfrac{2}{180}.\pi r$; let this distance be d''. Then the length (L) of the projected meridian θ between the parallels $(\phi+1)$ and $(\phi-1)$ is given (very nearly) by the relation $L^2=(d')^2+(d'')^2$. But the true distance between these same parallels is $\dfrac{2}{180}.\pi r$. The exaggeration in the meridian scale at the point (ϕ, θ) may thus be expressed as $\dfrac{L}{\frac{2}{180}.\pi r}$. In *Fig. 30*, this exaggeration is shown graphically for the parallels of latitude 15°, 30°, 45°, 60°, and 75°, and for meridians of longitude between 0° and 180°.

The projection of the complete globe is shown in *Fig. 31*, from which it will be at once evident that there are serious difficulties concerning the question of shape in those parts of the projection which lie diagonally away from the centre. For certain smaller regions, however, the projection is admirable; thus, Africa, which is 'balanced' on the equator, is projected very well indeed if the central meridian is situated in about longitude 20° E.; so also is South America if the central meridian is placed in longitude

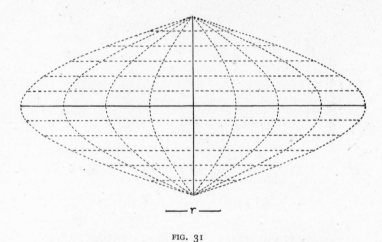

FIG. 31

SANSON-FLAMSTEED'S (SINUSOIDAL) PROJECTION

Parallels at intervals of 15°; meridians at intervals of 45°.

60° W. In these latter cases a good general map results, for the scale is correct along all parallels and the central meridian; the scale along other meridians is only slightly exaggerated; the equal-area property is preserved; the intersections of parallels with meridians are nearly rectangular, so shape is quite good, and direction fairly easily discernible.

Summary of Properties. Whatever the extent of the region mapped, the *equal-area* property is preserved. The scale along all parallels and the central meridian is true; the scale along other meridians increases as the obliquity of the intersections of meridians with parallels increases. Although not highly satisfactory for the projection of the whole globe, on account of the gross deformation of shape diagonally away from the centre, quite large regions can be projected with success; for example, Africa and South America.

Limitations. This is undoubtedly a valuable projection, although it is not really suitable for world maps, on account of the varying meridian scale and the consequent deformation of shape, illustrated, for example, in the case of New Zealand when the central meridian passes through Greenwich.

Construction. The equator is projected as a straight line, and at its true length, namely, $2\pi r$. The central meridian is also projected at its true length, as a straight line which both bisects, and is bisected by, the equator. The central meridian is correctly divided for the spacing of selected parallels, which are then drawn, at their true lengths, as straight lines parallel to the equator. Thus, the distance along the central meridian between the parallels ϕ' and ϕ'' is $\dfrac{\phi'-\phi''}{180}.\pi r$; and the length of the parallel ϕ is $2\pi r.\cos\phi$. Each parallel is correctly divided for the spacing of selected meridians, which are then drawn as (sine) curves through corresponding points on the divided parallels.

MOLLWEIDE'S PROJECTION

This is an *equal-area* projection designed to show the whole globe on one map. The distortion of *shape*, although admittedly great away from the centre of the map, is not so pronounced as in *Sanson-Flamsteed's Projection*, a factor of considerable importance in the choice of a world map. The better shape, however, is achieved at the expense of certain other properties, which in some cases are of greater importance.

The parallels of latitude are all projected as straight lines, which are, however, neither true to scale, nor uniformly spaced along the central meridian. The meridians are, in general, ellipses. (The central meridian is actually a straight line, and the meridians 90°E. and 90°W. together make a circle; these may both be regarded as special cases of the ellipse.) Thus, although accuracy of scale is sacrificed along both parallels and meridians, the particular method of construction does ensure the preservation of *equal-area*, which is the predominant property of the projection.

In *Fig. 32*, let the circle *NCSD* be drawn equal in *area* to one-half the surface area of the 'generating' globe. Thus, if R be the radius of this circle, and r the radius of the globe, then $R=r\sqrt{2}$. One diameter (*NS*) of this circle is the *central* meridian; the perpendicular diameter, produced equally in both directions to twice its original length, is the equator (AB). The ellipse $NASB$ then gives the total area of the complete globe, for:

$area$ of ellipse $NASB = 2 \times area$ of circle $NCSD$
$\qquad\qquad\qquad = 2 \times area$ of hemisphere of globe
$\qquad\qquad\qquad = area$ of globe.

Let PQ be the projection of the parallel ϕ, and let $\angle DOH = \alpha$. On the globe, the $area$ of the surface zone between the equator and the parallel ϕ is $2\pi r^2 . \sin \phi$; on the projection, this same zone is

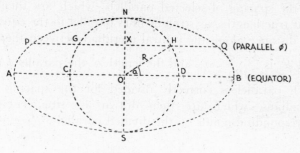

FIG. 32

MOLLWEIDE'S PROJECTION

cf. FIG. 33.

represented by the $area\ PABQ$, which is equal to twice the $area$ $GCDH$. The position of PQ is therefore determined by the condition:

$$2\pi r^2 . \sin \phi = 2 \times area\ GCDH$$
$$= 4 \times area\ XHDO$$
$$= 4 \times (\text{triangle } OXH + \text{sector } OHD)$$
$$= 4 \times (\tfrac{1}{2} R^2 . \sin \alpha . \cos \alpha + \tfrac{1}{2} R^2 \alpha^c)$$
$$= R^2 (\sin 2\alpha + 2\alpha^c)$$
$$= 2r^2 (\sin 2\alpha + 2\alpha^c)$$

whence $\pi . \sin \phi = \sin 2\alpha + 2\alpha^c)$.

By giving selected values to α, between $0°$ and $90°$, the corresponding values of ϕ can be determined, and a graph drawn to show the relation between α and ϕ, as in *Fig. 33*. Then, for any selected parallel ϕ, the corresponding value of α can be read from the graph. The parallel ϕ can thus be constructed at its appropriate distance from the equator.

All parallels are bounded by the ellipse $NASB$, for on that condition depends the *equal-area* property. Each parallel is divided uniformly throughout its length for the points of intersection with selected meridians, which are then drawn as curves through corresponding points on the parallels. Quite clearly, no one scale is applicable to the entire map, for each parallel has its own scale; nor is the scale along the equator true to the globe from which the projection has been derived. The scale along the meridians increases away from the central meridian, which, in total length, is projected on the same scale as the equator.

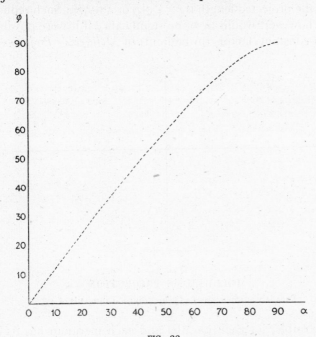

FIG. 33

MOLLWEIDE'S PROJECTION

Graph to show the relation between the parallel of latitude ϕ and the angle α used in the construction of the graticule.   *cf.* FIG. 32.

In view of the lack of uniformity in the scale, the projection does not possess the advantages of *Sanson-Flamsteed's Projection* when applied to smaller areas (for example, Africa), but it does provide a serviceable world map, which achieves a fair measure of compromise, and which is especially valuable for distributional purposes.

The projection of the complete globe is shown in *Fig. 34.*

Summary of Properties. Over the entire projection the *equal-area* property is preserved. In the case of the world map, the representation of shape is better than in *Sanson-Flamsteed's Projection*; but over a large area away from the centre, where the intersections of meridians with parallels are oblique, there is considerable deformation.

Limitations. There is a complete absence of any uniformity in the scale, although the projected total lengths of the equator and central meridian are strictly comparable, but slightly reduced from their true values (the true length of the equator is $2\pi r$, or $6\cdot283r$; the projected length is $r\times4\sqrt{2}$, or $5\cdot657r$). Such reduction as this, however, would be of no significance if it were possible to apply a constant 'factor' throughout; in *Mollweide's Projection* that

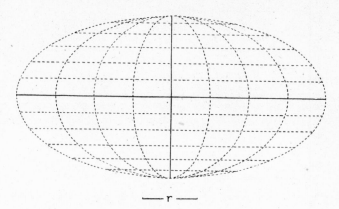

$\longmapsto r \longmapsto$

FIG. 34
MOLLWEIDE'S PROJECTION
Parallels at intervals of 15°; meridians at intervals of 45°.

is not possible, for each parallel and each meridian has its own particular scale and in the case of the meridians, the scale varies with latitude. The projection is of restricted use, therefore, except for distributional purposes which demand a comparison of areas.

Construction. The equator is projected as a straight line, $r\times4\sqrt{2}$ units in length, where r is the radius of the 'generating' globe. The central meridian is also projected as a straight line, perpendicular to, and half the length of, the equator. The complete globe is then represented by the ellipse whose major axis is the projected equator, and whose minor axis is the projected central meridian. Every parallel of latitude is bounded by this ellipse. The distance of the parallel ϕ from the projected equator is given by the relation: $\pi.\sin\phi=\sin 2\alpha+2\alpha^c$, where α is defined as in *Fig. 32.* Each parallel is then divided uniformly throughout its entire length for the points of intersection with selected meridians, which are drawn as curves (ellipses) through corresponding points of division.

PART II

CHAPTER VI
ZENITHAL (AZIMUTHAL) PROJECTIONS
EQUATORIAL AND OBLIQUE CASES

PERSPECTIVE

THE *polar* cases of the *zenithal* projections, discussed on p. 7 *et seq.*, are comparatively simple to visualize and construct, for the parallels of latitude are concentric circles, and the meridians of longitude are radii. Now, although the *equatorial* and *oblique* cases are more complicated, in that the necessary calculations are rather more involved, the underlying principles remain unaltered.

THE GNOMONIC PROJECTION

Equatorial Case. In the *equatorial* case of the *gnomonic*, the equator, which is a great circle, is projected as a straight line running across the middle of the map; the meridians, which are also great circles, are projected as straight lines perpendicular to the equator.

In *Fig. 35*, let E be the point where the *central* meridian intersects the equator; that is, the point where the plane of projection may be regarded as touching the 'generating' globe. Let P be a point on the equator in longitude θ; and let P′ be the *gnomonic* projection of P. Then $EP' = r.\tan θ$. The projected meridian in longitude θ therefore intersects the equator at a distance of $r.\tan θ$ from the central meridian. The spacing of selected meridians along the equator may thus be determined quite simply, by reference to tables of natural tangents. In a similar way it may be shown that the parallel φ intersects the central meridian at a distance of $r.\tan φ$ from the equator.

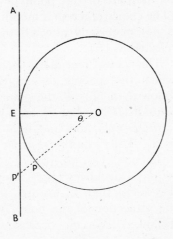

FIG. 35

73

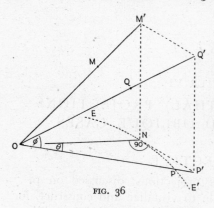

FIG. 36

The points of intersection of selected parallels (ϕ) with selected meridians (θ) may be determined as follows. In *Fig. 36*, let O be the centre of the 'generating' globe; EE' a part of the equator; $NM'Q'P'$ the plane which is tangential to the globe at N; P a point on the equator in longitude θ; and P' the *gnomonic* projection of P. Then: $\angle ONP' = 90°$, and $\angle NOP' = \angle NOP = \theta°$.

Let Q be a point on the globe in latitude ϕ and longitude θ; and let Q' be its *gnomonic* projection.
Then: $\angle Q'OP' = \angle QOP = \phi°$.
Therefore, in the triangle ONP', $OP' = r.\sec\theta$
and, in the triangle $Q'OP'$, $Q'P' = OP'.\tan\phi$
$$= r.\sec\theta.\tan\phi.$$

Thus the point of intersection of any selected parallel with any selected meridian can be readily determined. The parallels are drawn as smooth curves through corresponding points on the meridians, as in *Fig. 37*, which has been developed from a globe of radius r.

Oblique Case. In the *oblique* case, the plane of projection is tangential at some point between the equator and the poles; let the latitude of this point be $L°$N., and let its longitude be $O°$. (The choice of a *central* meridian is quite arbitrary, so the problem is not materially affected by denoting the particular meridian selected as $O°$.)

The central meridian ($O°$) is projected as a straight line, along which the spacing of selected parallels may be determined as follows. In *Fig. 38*, the plane of projection is tangential at A, in latitude $L°$N. Let P be a point on the globe in latitude ϕ ($\angle POE = \phi°$) and longitude O (that is, on the same meridian as A). Let P' be the *gnomonic* projection of P.

Then: $P'A = r.\tan(\phi-L)°$. Clearly, if ϕ is greater than L, the required distances ($P'A$) must be marked off towards the pole; if ϕ is less than L, towards the equator. From this relationship the projection of the pole (N) can thus be determined, for the distance AN' can be calculated, namely, $r.\tan(90-L)°$, or $r.\cot L°$.

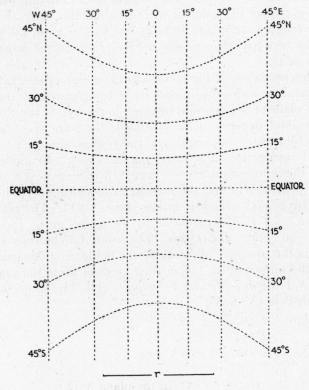

FIG. 37

GNOMONIC (EQUATORIAL CASE)

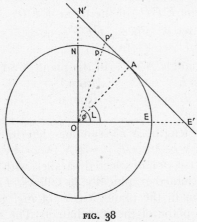

FIG. 38

All meridians are projected as straight lines radiating from N' (the projection of the pole) at their true angular intervals; that is, if the selected meridians occur at intervals of $x°$ on the globe, the angles between adjacent selected meridians on the projection will also be $x°$.

The determination of the points of intersection of selected projected parallels with other meridians is complicated by the fact that the plane of projection is inclined to the axis of the globe at an angle which depends on the latitude of the point of contact.

Fig. 39 illustrates, in perspective, the *gnomonic* projection of the points of intersection of selected parallels with two meridians, namely, the central meridian (indicated by the curve NCS, which is in the plane $N'SY$) and the meridian in longitude θ (indicated by the curve NDS, which is in the plane $N'SX$). The plane of projection $(XN'Y)$ is tangential to the globe at C; therefore $\angle N'CO = 90°$, and $\angle D'CO = 90°$. The points A (in latitude $\phi°$N.), and F (on the equator), all lie along the meridian in longitude θ, also on the surface of the globe; their *gnomonic* projections on the plane $XN'Y$ are B', D', and F' respectively. The projection of the North Pole (N) is N'.

Therefore $\angle E'OC = \angle F'OD' = L°$;
$$\angle E'OA' = \angle F'OB' = \phi°;$$
$$\angle E'ON' = \angle F'ON' = 90°;$$
$$\angle E'OF' = \theta°$$

Then, in the triangle $N'CO$ (in the plane $N'SY$),
$$N'O = OC.\sec (90-L)° = r.\operatorname{cosec} L° \quad\dots\dots\dots\dots\dots \text{(i)}$$
and, in the triangle COE' (in the plane $N'SY$),
$$E'O = OC.\sec L° = r.\sec L° \quad\dots\dots\dots\dots\dots\dots \text{(ii)}$$
and, in the triangle $E'F'O$ (in the plane $E'F'O$),
$$F'O = OE'.\sec \theta° \text{ (since } \angle OE'F' = 90°),$$
$$= r.\sec L°.\sec \theta° \text{ (from ii)} \quad\dots\dots\dots\dots\dots \text{(iii)}$$
Thus, in the triangle $N'OF'$ (in the plane $N'SX$),
$$N'O = r.\cos L° \dots\dots\dots \text{(from i)}$$
$$F'O = r.\sec L°.\sec \theta° \ \dots \text{(from iii)} \Big\} \dots\dots\dots\dots \text{(iv)}$$
$$\angle N'OF' = 90°.$$

Therefore the length $N'F'$ can be determined, either by calculation, for $(N'F')^2 = (OF')^2 + (ON')^2$, or by scale-drawing. The points of intersection of selected parallels with the meridian θ may now be determined graphically, as follows. *Fig. 40* shows the *gnomonic* projection in the plane $N'OX$ (of *Fig. 39*); that is, the projection in the plane of the meridian θ. The curve FBN, an

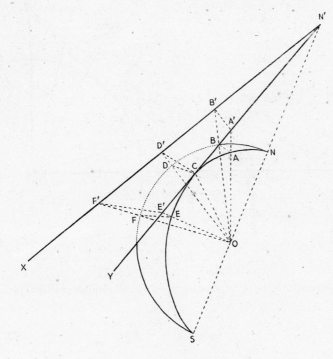

FIG. 39

GNOMONIC (OBLIQUE CASE)

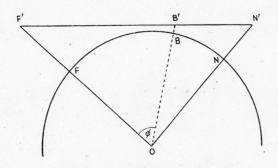

FIG. 40

GNOMONIC (OBLIQUE CASE)

The point of contact of the plane of projection with the 'generating' globe is in latitude 45° N and in longitude 0°. F'ON' is in the plane of the meridian 30° E or W. B' is the projection of the point B (lat. 60° N.; long. 30° E or W.)

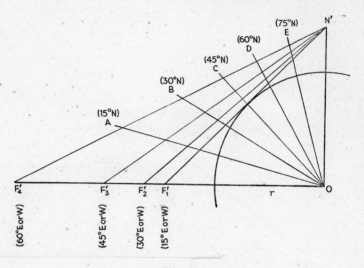

FIG. 41 ·

GNOMONIC (OBLIQUE CASE)

Determination of the points of intersection of selected parallels and meridians.

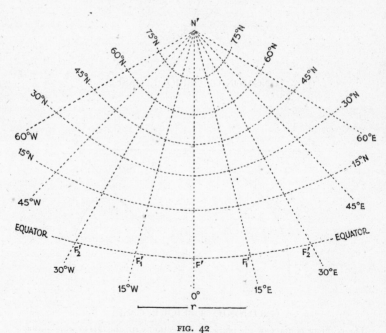

FIG. 42

GNOMONIC (OBLIQUE CASE)

The plane of projection is tangential to the globe at the point where the central meridian intersects the parallel in latitude 45° N.

arc of a circle of radius r, represents the surface of the globe along the meridian θ; $F'N'$ represents the projection of the meridian on the given plane, drawn so as to conform to the requirements of the three equations bracketed in (iv)(above). It will be noticed that corresponding points in *Figs. 39 and 40* are easily distinguishable, for the lettering is similar in the two cases. Thus, in *Fig. 40*, N is the pole, and N' its projection; F is the point where the meridian θ crosses the equator, and F' its projection; B is the point where the meridian θ crosses the parallel ϕ, and B' its projection. The distance $F'B'$ is determined by measuring off the angle $\angle FOB$ equal to ϕ, and producing the 'ray' OB to cut $F'N'$ in B'. The distance along the meridian θ from the equator to the point of intersection of the parallel ϕ with the meridian θ can thus be evaluated when ϕ and θ are given specific values.

One method of solution is illustrated in *Fig. 41*, in which it should be a comparatively simple matter to identify the points in question, on account of the correspondence of the lettering in this and previous diagrams. By giving appropriate values to θ in equation (iii) (above), the line $F'N'$ can be drawn for any selected meridian, as shown in the diagram; and the required distances (AF, BF, etc.) can then be measured. *Figs. 41 and 42*, studied together, should make the method clear. The whole projection, to any prescribed boundary, can thus be completed as in *Fig. 42*, in which both meridians and parallels are shown at intervals of 15°.

THE STEREOGRAPHIC PROJECTION

Equatorial Case. The equator and the central meridian are projected as straight lines, intersecting at right angles at the centre of the projection.

The point of intersection of the parallel ϕ with the central meridian is given by the relation $y = 2r.\tan \frac{1}{2}\phi$, where y is the distance from the centre of the projection. The point of intersection of the meridian θ with the equator is given by the relation $x = 2r.\tan \frac{1}{2}\theta$, where x is the distance from the centre of the projection. In both these cases, therefore, the points of intersection may be determined by reference to tables of natural tangents; the 'symmetry' along the two perpendicular axes is apparent.

The point of intersection of the parallel ϕ with the meridian θ may be determined as follows. In *Fig. 43*, $EPQF$ represents a part of the surface of the globe bounded by the equator (EP), the parallel ϕ (*FQ*), the central meridian (*EF*), and the meridian θ (*PQ*). *EP'Q'F'* is the plane of projection which is tangential to the globe at *E*, which is thus the centre of the projection. *O* is the centre of the globe, and *C* the point of origin of the projection;

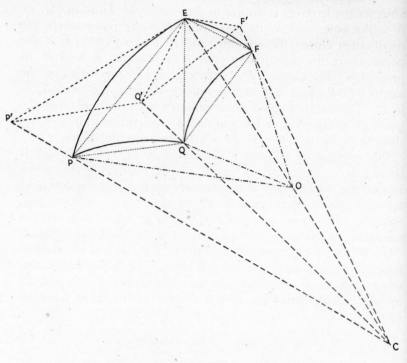

FIG. 43

STEREOGRAPHIC (EQUATORIAL CASE)

EPQF is a part of the surface of the globe bounded by the equator (*EP*),
the parallel ϕ (*FQ*), the central meridian (*EF*) and the meridian θ (*PQ*).
The projection of *P* is *P'*; that of *Q* is *Q'*; and that of *F* is *F'*.

P', *Q'*, and *F'* are the *stereographic* projections of *P*, *Q*, and *F* respectively. The line *EOC* is thus an equatorial diameter of the globe, while *OE*, *OF*, *OP*, and *OQ* are all radii.

Then $\angle EOF = \angle POQ = \phi$; and $\angle EOP = \theta$,
but in the triangle *P'EC*, $\angle P'EC = 90°$, $\angle P'CE = \frac{1}{2}\theta$, and *EC* = 2r.
Therefore $P'E = 2r.\tan \frac{1}{2}\theta$ (= *x* as defined above).

Also, in the triangle *EF'C*, $\angle F'EC = 90°$, $\angle F'CE = \frac{1}{2}\phi$, and *EC* = 2r.
Therefore $F'E = 2r.\tan \frac{1}{2}\phi$ (= *y* as defined above).

Now let $\angle EOQ=q$; then in the triangle $EQ'C$, $\angle Q'EC=90°$, $\angle Q'CE=\tfrac{1}{2}q$, and $EC=2r$; whence $Q'E=2r.\tan \tfrac{1}{2}q$ .... (i)

But in the plane $PEFQ$, the chord $PE =2r.\sin \tfrac{1}{2}\theta$;

the chord $QF=2r.\cos \phi.\sin \tfrac{1}{2}\theta$;

the chord $EF=$the chord $PQ=2r.\sin \tfrac{1}{2}\phi$.

Thus, for any selected values of ϕ and θ, the lengths of PE, QF, EF, and PQ can be determined; and hence the value of EQ can

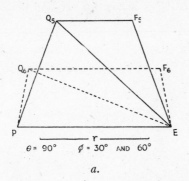

$\theta = 90°$ $\phi = 30°$ AND $60°$

a.

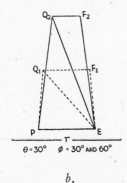

$\theta = 30°$ $\phi = 30°$ AND $60°$

b.

$\theta = 60°$ $\phi = 30°$ AND $60°$

c.

FIG. 44

be calculated, for $EQ^2=PQ^2+PE.QF$. (Alternatively, a scale-drawing can be made, and EQ measured, as in *Fig. 44 a, b, c.*)

In the triangle EQC, $\angle EQC=90°$, $\angle ECQ=\tfrac{1}{2}q$, and $EC=2r$; therefore $EQ=2r.\sin \tfrac{1}{2}q$, whence $\sin \tfrac{1}{2}q$ (and hence q) can be determined, for the value of EQ is now known for any selected values of ϕ and θ. Then, $Q'E$ can be determined from equation (i) (above); in other words, the *radial distance* from the centre of the projection to the point of intersection of the parallel ϕ with the meridian θ can be readily determined. Alternatively, a graphical

6

method of determining $Q'E$ is available, as illustrated in *Fig. 45*, in which $EC=2r$, EL is drawn at right angles to EC, and EDC is a semicircle. With centre E, and radii as given by each of the diagonals of *Fig. 44* in turn, strike arcs to cut the semicircle in Q_1, Q_2, Q_3, etc. Join CQ_1, CQ_2, CQ_3, etc., and produce the lines to cut EL in Q'_1, Q'_2, Q'_3, etc. Then EQ'_1, EQ'_2, EQ'_3, etc., are the required distances. Thus, in the triangle ECQ_1, for example, $EQ_1=EC.\sin \angle ECQ_1 = 2r.\sin \frac{1}{2}q$; and in the triangle ECQ'_1, $EQ'_1=EC.\tan \angle ECQ'_1 = 2r.\tan \frac{1}{2}q$. It will be noticed that these

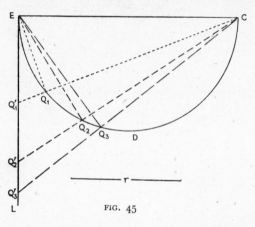

FIG. 45

expressions for EQ_1 (a particular value of EQ) and EQ'_1 (a particular value of EQ') are identical with those given above. *Figs. 44 and 45* are drawn on the same scale, and lettered so that corresponding points may be easily identified.

In *Fig. 46*, the points F, Q, and Q' (of *Fig. 43*) are shown projected perpendicularly on to the plane of the equator, where they occupy the positions F_1, Q_1, and Q'_1 respectively. The diagram thus shows the perpendicular distances of the various points from the plane of the central meridian. But $OE=OP=r$; $EC=2r$; $OF_1=OQ_1=r.\cos \phi$; and $\angle EOP = \angle F_1OQ_1 = \theta$. Therefore $Q_1K = OQ_1.\sin \angle KOQ_1 = r.\cos \phi.\sin \theta$; and $OK= OQ_1.\cos \angle KOQ_1= r.\cos \phi.\cos \theta$.

But in the similar triangles ECQ'_1 and KCQ_1, $\dfrac{EQ'_1}{KQ_1}=\dfrac{EC}{KC}$;

therefore $EQ'_1=\dfrac{EC.KQ_1}{KC}=\dfrac{2r \times r.\cos \phi.\sin \theta}{r+r.\cos \phi.\cos \theta}$

$$=\frac{2r.\cos \phi.\sin \theta}{1+ \cos \phi.\cos \theta} \quad \dots\dots\dots\dots\dots\dots \text{(ii)}$$

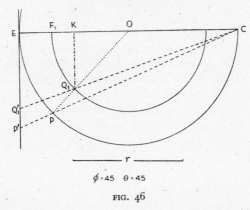

$\phi = 45 \quad \theta = 45$

FIG. 46

The position of Q' on the projection is thus defined by the two equations (i) and (ii) given above; namely, Q', the projection of the point Q (ϕ, θ), lies at a *radial distance* of $2r.\tan\frac{1}{2}q$ (where $q = \angle EOQ$ of *Fig. 43*) from the centre of the projection, and at a *perpendicular distance* of $\dfrac{2r.\cos\phi.\sin\theta}{1 + \cos\phi.\cos\theta}$ from the central meridian.

The projection of a complete hemisphere is shown in *Fig. 47*, in which two important properties of the *stereographic* are at once

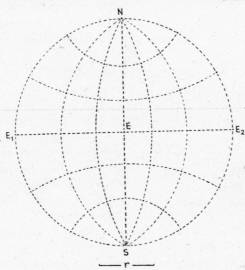

FIG. 47

STEREOGRAPHIC (EQUATORIAL CASE)

The equator is represented by E_1EE_2; the central meridian by *NES*.
Parallels and meridians at intervals of 30°.

evident; namely, (i) all meridians intersect all parallels at right angles, (ii) all meridians and all parallels are projected as true arcs of circles. (The central meridian and the equator, which are projected as straight lines, because they are great circles passing through both the point of origin and the point of contact, may be regarded as special cases of the circle.) These two properties are particular examples of the more general characteristics associated with zenithal orthomorphic projection, which, it will be recalled, ensures correct representation of shape at any point over the entire area.

Oblique Case. The central meridian is once again projected as a straight line. The great circle through the point of contact and the point of origin, at right angles to the plane of the central meridian, is also projected as a straight line, at right angles to the projection of the central meridian; but this great circle is not a parallel of latitude. All parallels of latitude, including the equator, and all meridians other than the central meridian, are projected as arcs of circles.

In *Fig. 48*, which represents a section through the centre of the globe, at right angles to the plane of projection, let the point of

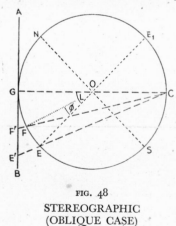

FIG. 48
STEREOGRAPHIC
(OBLIQUE CASE)

contact of the plane of projection with the globe be in latitude $L°$N., and let F be a point on the central meridian in latitude ϕ; thus, $\angle EOG = L°$, $\angle EOF = \phi°$, and $\angle FOG = (L-\phi)°$. Now, in the triangle GCF', $\angle CGF' = 90°$, $\angle GCF' = \frac{1}{2}(L-\phi)$, and $GC = 2r$; therefore $GF' = 2r.\tan \frac{1}{2}(L-\phi)$. The points of intersection of all parallels with the central meridian can thus be plotted quite simply by reference to tables of natural tangents. [If ϕ is greater than L, then $GF' = 2r.\tan\frac{1}{2}(\phi-L)$; and if F and G are on opposite sides of the equator, then $GF' = 2r.\tan\frac{1}{2}(L+\phi)$.]

In *Fig. 49*, G is the point of contact of the plane of projection with the globe, O is the centre of the globe, and C is the point of origin of the projection; thus, GOC is a diameter of the globe. The plane of the equator is represented by SES', the plane of the great circle through G and C by SGS', the plane of the parallel of latitude ($L°$N.) through G by TGT', the plane of the central meridian by EOD, and the plane of the meridian in longitude θ by MOD. Q is the point where the great circle SGS' intersects the meridian θ; Q' is the *stereographic* projection of Q on to the plane which is tangential to the globe at G. The plane of the great circle SGS' is perpendicular to the plane of the central

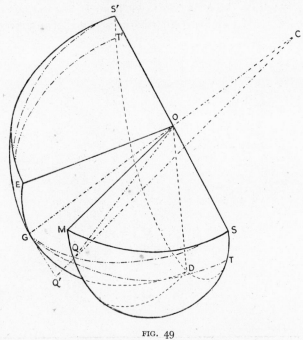

FIG. 49

STEREOGRAPHIC (OBLIQUE CASE)

meridian (EOD); therefore GQ' gives the projected distance, at right angles to the projected central meridian, from the centre G to the point of intersection of the meridian θ with the great circle SGS'. Thus, by giving specific values to θ, that is, by selecting specific meridians, the perpendicular distance from Q to the central meridian may be determined as follows.

Let r be the radius of the 'generating' globe, and let the plane of projection be tangential in latitude $45°$N. In *Fig. 50*, the planes SGS' and TGT' (of *Fig. 49*) have been 'projected' perpendicularly on to the plane of the equator (SES' in *Fig. 49*). The plane TGT', which is a circle parallel to the plane of the equator, has been 'projected' into a circle of radius $r.\cos 45°$, since G is in latitude

45°N. The two circles, one representing the equator (radius r), and the other representing the parallel of latitude 45°N. (radius $r.\cos 45°$), are clearly concentric, as shown in *Fig. 50*. The plane *SGS'*, which, on the globe, is a circle inclined at an angle of 45° to the plane of the equator, has been 'projected' into an ellipse, of which the major axis (*SOS'*) is $2r$, and the minor axis (G_1OC_1) $2r.\cos 45°$. Such an ellipse can be accurately plotted.

In *Fig. 50*, 'rays' have been drawn from O at intervals of 30°; the lines OE, OM_1, etc., are therefore the lines of intersection of

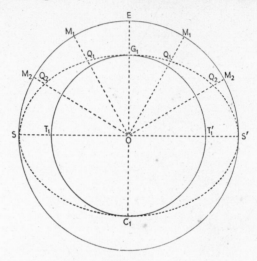

FIG. 50

The radii of the two circles are r and $r.\cos 45°$.

The equation of the ellipse is $\dfrac{x^2}{r^2} + \dfrac{y^2}{(r.\cos\ 45)^2} = 1$

By giving different values to y (along OE), the corresponding values of x (along OS') can be calculated, and the ellipse plotted.

selected meridian planes with the plane of the equator. The points of intersection of these 'rays' with the ellipse thus give the perpendicular distance of Q from the plane of the central meridian. (For example, when $\theta = 30°$, the perpendicular distance of Q from the plane of the central meridian is $OQ_1.\sin 30°$; when $\theta = 60°$, the distance is $OQ_2.\sin 60°$; and so on.) For any selected meridian the perpendicular distance of Q from the plane of the central meridian is therefore readily determined. But the plane *SGS'* (in *Fig. 49*) is perpendicular to the plane of the central meridian; that is, the plane of the triangle *CGQ'* is perpendicular to the plane *EOD*. Let the perpendicular distance of Q from the plane of the central meridian be d, when θ has some specific value. Then $d = OQ.\sin \angle GOQ = r.\sin \angle GOQ$; whence $\angle GOQ$ can be determined. But $\angle GOQ = 2.\angle GCQ$; hence, in the triangle GCQ',

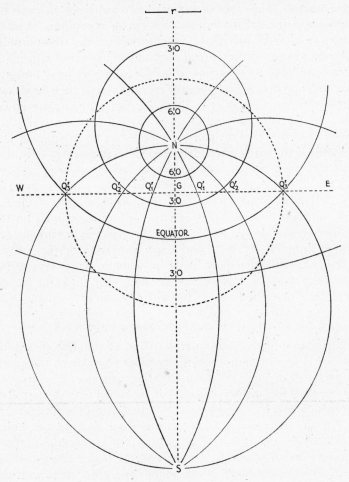

FIG. 51

STEREOGRAPHIC (OBLIQUE CASE)

The plane of projection is in latitude 45° N.

$\angle CGQ' = 90°$, $GC = 2r$, and $\angle GCQ'$ can be determined; then $GQ' = 2r.\tan \angle GCQ'$. Thus the points of intersection of selected meridians with the straight line through the centre of the projection, at right angles to the central meridian, can be plotted. The projection can then be completed, as in *Fig. 51*.

The central meridian and the great circle through the point of contact of the plane of projection with the globe and the point of origin of the projection are drawn as straight lines, intersecting at right angles. The central meridian is divided for the selected parallels, and the great circle is divided for the points of intersection of selected meridians, according to the relationships established above. If the central meridian is extended sufficiently far, it is possible to plot pairs of points for each parallel of latitude; circles, their centres on the central meridian, can then be drawn through corresponding pairs. Thus, in *Fig. 51*, complete circles are shown for latitudes 30°N. and 60°N. Alternatively, the positions of corresponding pairs of points can be calculated, and the centre of the circle then determined in each case; only that part of the circle which is necessary for the map need then be drawn, as in the case of the equator and the parallel 30°S. in *Fig. 51*. The selected meridians are drawn as arcs of circles, passing through the two poles and the appropriate point on the prescribed great circle. In *Fig. 51*, the selected meridians are drawn at intervals of 30°, both east and west of the central meridian. Finally, that part of the projection which is required for the map may be framed, as shown in the diagram by the broken circle described about the centre of the projection.

THE ORTHOGRAPHIC PROJECTION

Equatorial Case. The central meridian and all parallels of latitude lie, on the globe, in planes which are perpendicular to the plane of projection; in view of the particular method of projection, therefore, they will all be projected as straight lines; the parallels are perpendicular to, and bisected by, the central meridian.

Meridians, other than the central meridian, lie in planes which are inclined to the plane of projection; their circular outlines must, therefore, be projected as ellipses, the major axes of which are equal to the diameter of the globe, and coincident with the central meridian. The problems involved in the construction can thus be resolved in a determination of (i) the spacing between selected parallels along the central meridian, and (ii) the lengths of the minor axes of the projected ellipses of selected meridians.

In *Fig. 52*, which represents a section through the centre of the globe, parallel to the plane of projection, the spacing of the parallels of latitude along the axis, and hence along the central meridian of the projection, is given by the relation $y = r.\sin \phi$, where y is the distance of the parallel ϕ from the centre. The

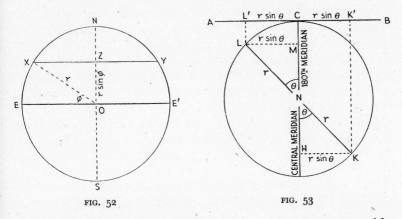

FIG. 52   FIG. 53

parallels of latitude can therefore be drawn by reference to tables of natural sines.

In *Fig. 53*, which represents a section in the plane of the equator, and hence at right angles to the plane of projection, the length of the minor axis of the projected meridian θ is clearly $r.\sin θ$. Moreover, it will be apparent that the projection of the meridian in longitude θ° *east*, and the projection of the meridian in longitude θ° *west*, together make a complete ellipse.

The projection of a complete hemisphere is shown in *Fig. 54*, in which both meridians and parallels are drawn at intervals of 30°.

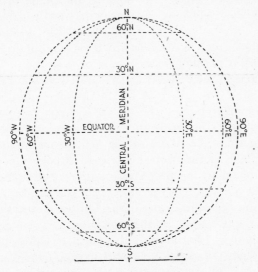

FIG. 54
ORTHOGRAPHIC (EQUATORIAL CASE)

Oblique Case. The central meridian is again projected as a straight line; but all other meridians, and all parallels, are projected as ellipses. The centres of the projected parallels (ellipses) all lie along the central meridian; the major axes are at right angles to the central meridian. The diameter of the parallel ϕ on the globe is $2r.\cos \phi$, which is also the length of the major axis of the projected ellipse.

In *Fig. 55*, which represents a section through the centre of the globe, in the plane of the central meridian, the plane of projection

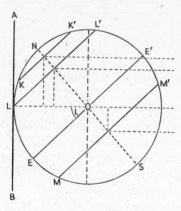

is tangential to the globe in latitude $L°$ N. The length of the minor axis of the projected ellipse in latitude ϕ is then $2r.\cos \phi.\sin L$; and the distance of the centre of the ellipse from the centre of the projection is $r.\sin \phi.\cos L$. The required ellipse can thus be constructed, for the position of its centre, and the lengths and directions of its axes, are all known.

The meridians on the globe, other than the central meridian, lie in planes which are inclined both to the plane of the central meridian and to the plane of projection. Yet, in each of these meridian planes there is one line which, passing through the centre of the globe, is parallel to the plane of projection. This line is the major axis of the projected meridian ellipse, and is clearly $2r$ units in length. The centres of all the meridian ellipses are at the centre of the projection.

FIG. 55
ORTHOGRAPHIC
(OBLIQUE CASE)

At the equator, the perpendicular distance on the globe of the meridian θ, from the plane of the central meridian, is $r.\sin \theta$. Since the plane of the central meridian is perpendicular to the plane of projection, the projected position of the point of intersection of the meridian θ with the equator will also be at a distance of $r.\sin \theta$ from the central meridian. On the globe, all meridians intersect at the two poles; on the projection, they will also intersect at the two poles. (Normally, only one pole will appear on the projection, but the position of the second pole can easily be 'superimposed', for the arrangement is symmetrical. Thus, if the plane of projection is tangential to the globe at some point in the northern hemisphere, it would be convenient to project the North Pole; but the position of the South Pole, if projected under like conditions, would lie along the central meridian, at the same distance from the centre as the projected North Pole, but on the opposite side of the centre.) In the case of the meridians, the amount of information available is now sufficient to make possible

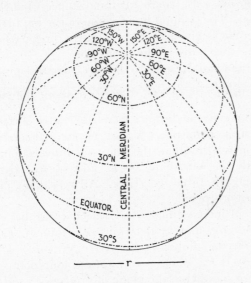

FIG. 56

ORTHOGRAPHIC (OBLIQUE CASE)

The plane of projection is tangential to the globe in latitude 45° N. Meridians and parallels at intervals of 30°.

the completion of the projection. For each selected meridian, it is possible to determine (i) the position of the centre of the projected ellipse, (ii) the length of the major axis, and (iii) the positions of three known points on the ellipse (namely, the two poles and the point of intersection of the meridian with the equator).

The projection of a complete hemisphere is shown in *Fig. 56*, in which the plane of projection is tangential to the globe in latitude 45°N., and in which both meridians and parallels are drawn at intervals of 30°.

NON-PERSPECTIVE

THE ZENITHAL EQUIDISTANT PROJECTION

Equatorial Case. The equator and the central meridian are projected as straight lines, perpendicular to one another. The point of intersection of the meridian θ with the equator is given by the relation $x = r.\theta^c$, where x is the distance from the centre of the projection. The point of intersection of the parallel ϕ with the central meridian is given by the relation $y = r.\phi^c$, where y is the distance from the centre of the projection.

The meridians 90° E. and 90° W. are together projected as a circle of radius $\dfrac{\pi.r}{2} (= \frac{1}{4}$ of $2\pi r)$, described about the centre of the projection; the extreme distance from the centre of the projection to the edge of the hemisphere is thus represented correctly. Since the projection is azimuthal, the points of intersection of selected parallels with the meridians 90° E. and 90° W. are uniformly spaced around the projected circle. All meridians must clearly pass through both poles.

The point of intersection of any selected parallel ϕ with any selected meridian θ may be determined as follows. Consider the four points on the globe: P_1 (ϕ°N., θ°W.), P_2 (ϕ°N., θ°E.), P_3 (ϕ°S., θ°W.), P_4 (ϕ°S., θ°E.). These four points lie in one plane, which is parallel to the plane of projection; and the chords joining the points form a rectangle, the centre of which lies on the line which passes through the centre of the globe and the centre of the projection.

Thus, the *chord* $P_1P_2 =$ the *chord* $P_3P_4 = 2r.\cos \phi.\sin \theta$
        the *chord* $P_1P_3 =$ the *chord* $P_2P_4 = 2r.\sin \phi$
the diagonals of the rectangle, namely, the *chords* P_1P_4 and P_2P_3, are equal, and each is equal to z, where

$$z = 2r.\sqrt{\sin^2\phi + \cos^2\phi.\sin^2\theta}.$$

Each diagonal therefore subtends at the centre of the globe an angle α, where $\alpha = 2\left(\sin^{-1}\dfrac{z}{2r}\right)$.

The *arc* distances on the globe, corresponding to these *chord* diagonals, are therefore equal to $r\alpha$. Both arcs pass through the point of intersection of the central meridian with the equator; that is, the point at which the plane of projection 'touches' the globe. The distance of each of the four points (P_1, P_2, P_3, P_4) from the centre of the projection is then known, for each is equal to $\frac{1}{2}r\alpha$. In order to 'fix' the positions of the four points on the projection, advantage may be taken of the azimuthal properties of the projection.

Thus, if the 'ray' from the centre of the projection to the point P_1 makes an angle $\angle q$ with the central meridian, this 'ray' will have the same bearing as the corresponding 'ray' on the globe.

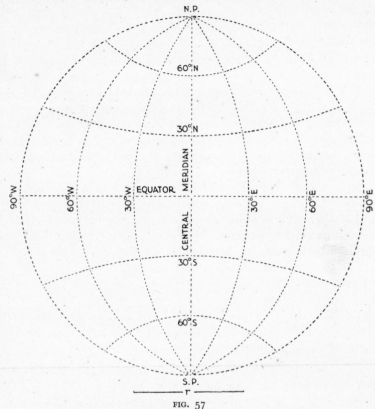

FIG. 57

ZENITHAL EQUIDISTANT (EQUATORIAL CASE)

Then $\tan \angle q = \dfrac{2r.\cos \phi.\sin \theta}{2r.\sin \phi} = \dfrac{\cos \phi.\sin \theta}{\sin \phi} = \cot \phi \sin \theta.$

The position of a point (ϕ, θ) on the projection can therefore be made subject to two conditions, which operate in combination: (i) the distance of the point from the centre, and (ii) the bearing of the point from the centre. For selected values of ϕ and θ, both conditions can now be evaluated.

The projection of a complete hemisphere is shown in *Fig. 57*, in which both meridians and parallels are drawn at intervals of 30°.

The *oblique case* is illustrated in *Fig. 63*, on p. 99.

THE ZENITHAL EQUAL-AREA PROJECTION

Equatorial Case. The equator and the central meridian are projected as straight lines, perpendicular to one another. The point of intersection of the meridian θ with the equator is given by the relation $x = r . \sqrt{2(1 - \cos \theta)}$, where x is the distance from the centre of the projection. The point of intersection of the parallel ϕ with the central meridian is given by the relation $y = r . \sqrt{2(1 - \cos \phi)}$, where y is the distance from the centre of the projection.

The meridians 90° E. and 90° W are together projected as a circle of radius $r\sqrt{2}$, described about the centre of the projection. The area of the projected hemisphere is therefore $\pi(r\sqrt{2})^2$, that is, $2\pi r^2$, which is the area of the hemisphere on the globe. Thus, so far as the complete hemisphere is concerned, the *equal-area* property is preserved.

Since the projection is azimuthal, the points of intersection of selected projected parallels with the projected meridians 90° E. and 90° W. are uniformly spaced around the bounding circle of the projected hemisphere. Moreover, all meridians must pass through both poles, the projections of which are known.

The point of intersection of any selected parallel (ϕ) with any selected meridian (θ) may be determined as follows. Consider the four points on the globe: P_1 ($\phi°$N., $\theta°$W.), P_2 ($\phi°$N., $\theta°$E.), P_3 ($\phi°$S., $\theta°$W.), P_4 ($\phi°$S., $\theta°$E.). Then, as in the case of the *zenithal equidistant*, discussed on p. 92, the length of the *chord* P_1P_4 (or P_2P_3) is equal to z, where

$$z = 2r . \sqrt{\sin^2\phi + \cos^2\phi . \sin^2\theta}.$$

But this chord is the diagonal of the rectangle formed by the four points, and it is also the diameter of the circle which passes through the four points. The angle subtended by the chord at the centre of the globe is therefore equal to α where $\alpha = 2\left(\sin^{-1}\dfrac{z}{2r}\right)$. The area of the globe, enclosed by the circle which passes through the four points, is $2\pi r^2 . (1 - \cos \alpha)$, and the distance of each of the four points from the centre of the projection is then $r . \sqrt{2(1 - \cos \alpha)}$. Finally, the 'ray' drawn from the centre of the projection to each of the four points makes with the central meridian an angle $\angle q$, where

$$\tan \angle q = \frac{\cos \phi . \sin \theta}{\sin \phi} = \cot \phi . \sin \theta.$$

The position of the point (ϕ, θ) on the projection can then be precisely determined, for it is subject to the combination of two conditions; namely, (i) distance from the centre of the projection,

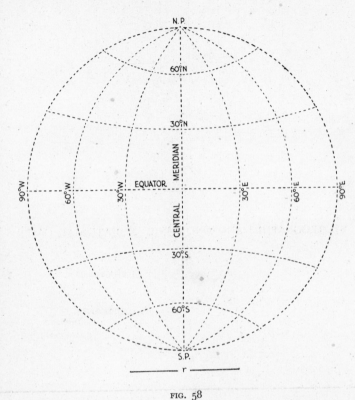

FIG. 58

ZENITHAL EQUAL-AREA (EQUATORIAL CASE)

and (ii) bearing from the centre. For selected values of ϕ and θ, both conditions can now be evaluated.

The projection of a complete hemisphere is shown in *Fig. 58*, in which both meridians and parallels are drawn at intervals of 30°.

The *oblique case* is illustrated in *Fig. 64* on p. 99.

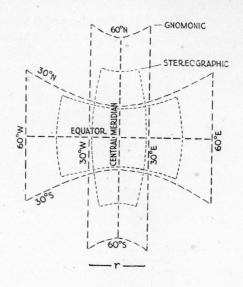

FIG. 59

STEREOGRAPHIC AND GNOMONIC (EQUATORIAL CASE)

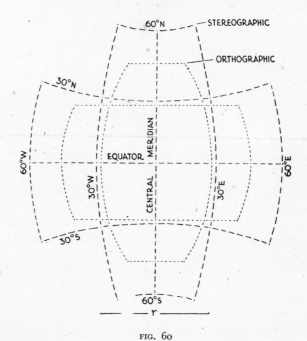

FIG. 60

STEREOGRAPHIC AND ORTHOGRAPHIC (EQUATORIAL CASE)

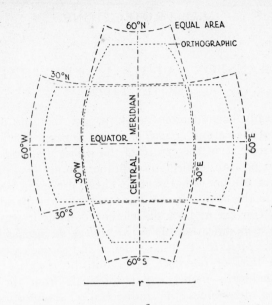

FIG. 61

ZENITHAL EQUAL-AREA AND ORTHOGRAPHIC
(EQUATORIAL CASE)

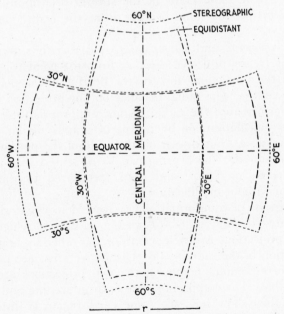

FIG. 62

ZENITHAL EQUIDISTANT AND STEREOGRAPHIC
(EQUATORIAL CASE)

TRANSFORMATION IN ZENITHAL
PROJECTION

IT has already been demonstrated (p. 25) that the distinctive properties of the various *zenithal projections* depend, in effect, upon the radial scale from the centre of the projection, and that one *zenithal* can be transformed into another simply by appropriate modification of the radial scale. These processes were easily visualized in the *polar cases*, for the meridians and parallels were themselves convenient lines of reference. Thus it was possible to refer to a modification of '*the scale along the meridians*', or '*the spacing of the parallels*'. In the *equatorial* and *oblique* cases no such convenient lines of reference exist, but the essential principle remains unaltered, namely, that the scale from the *centre of the projection* determines the individual characteristics of the projection. Moreover, the azimuthal properties of the zenithal projections facilitate the process of transformation, for, provided the *centre* is the same point in the several projections, a given point (ϕ, θ) has the same bearing from the centre on all the zenithals.

In the *equatorial* and *oblique* cases, it is therefore necessary to determine (i) the projected distance from the point (ϕ, θ) to the centre of the projection, and (ii) the bearing of the point (ϕ, θ) from the centre. The radial distance on one projection can then be transformed into the radial distance appropriate to another, either by calculation, or by means of graphs similar to those shown in *Fig. 11*, but drawn on the scale of the particular projections required. The bearing can be measured with reference to a selected meridian, and then transferred to the second projection without modification.

The process of transformation, as applied to equatorial cases, is illustrated in *Figs. 59, 60, 61, and 62*, in each of which, one of the two projections is developed from the other by appropriate modification of the radial scale. Distinctive areas are projected; hence, corresponding points on the two projections are clearly recognizable. The comparisons are both interesting and instructive, for they show how the same earth-region is distorted in different ways by different projections; they show, in fact, that a map should first be 'understood' before it is 'read', for there is always the danger of misinterpretation.

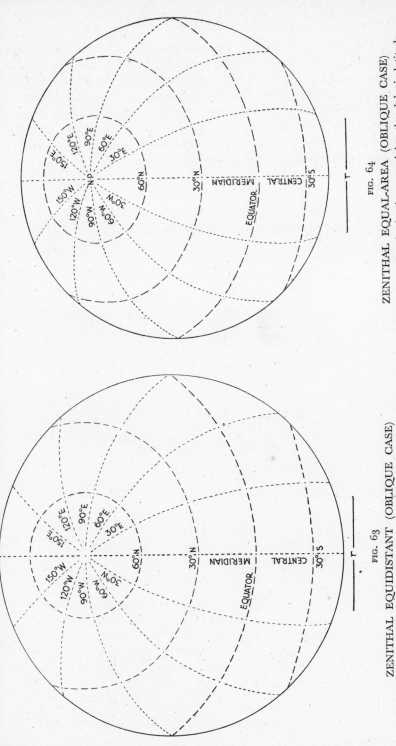

FIG. 64

ZENITHAL EQUAL-AREA (OBLIQUE CASE)

The plane of projection is tangential to the globe in latitude 45° N.

FIG. 63

ZENITHAL EQUIDISTANT (OBLIQUE CASE)

The plane of projection is tangential to the globe in latitude 45° N.

The same principle has been employed in the construction of the *oblique* cases of the *zenithal equidistant* (*Fig. 63*) and the *zenithal equal-area* (*Fig. 64*); both have been developed, by transformation of the radial scale, from the *oblique* case of the *stereographic* (*Fig. 51*). In the process of *zenithal* transformation, the *stereographic* is very useful, for its radial distances increase fairly uniformly, and do not suffer either the excessive exaggeration of the *gnomonic*, or the serious diminution of the *orthographic*.

CHAPTER VII

CONICAL PROJECTIONS

THE TWO-STANDARD EQUAL-AREA CONICAL PROJECTION

IN this projection, two selected parallels of latitude are made 'standard'; that is, both are projected at their true lengths, but as concentric arcs of circles, which are spaced at such a distance that the equal-area property is preserved. By making two parallels standard, it is possible to obtain a better distribution of general accuracy over a fairly large area than when only one is made standard. For most purposes, therefore, the two-standard conic would be preferred.

In *Fig. 25* (which is not drawn to scale), let PP', in latitude ϕ', and QQ', in latitude ϕ'', be the two projected standard parallels which satisfy the condition of *equal area*; and let r be the radius of the 'generating' globe.

Then the *arc* $PP' = 2\pi r.\cos \phi'$;
and the *arc* $QQ' = 2\pi r.\cos \phi''$.

But the area between these two projected arcs must equal the area between the same parallels of latitude on the globe; that is,

$$\text{area } PQQ'P' = 2\pi r^2(\sin \phi'' - \sin \phi').$$

Now let $\dfrac{\angle POP'\,°}{360}$ $\left(\text{or } \dfrac{\angle POP'\text{c}}{2\pi}\right) = k;$

let OQ, the radius of the projected parallel ϕ'', be $R_{\phi''}$; and let PQ, the distance between the parallels ϕ' and ϕ'', be d; then the area between the projected parallels ϕ' and ϕ'' is

$$k\pi[(R_{\phi''} + d)^2 - R_{\phi''}^2],$$

which equals $k\pi.(2R_{\phi''}.d + d^2)$, and which must be equated to the corresponding area on the globe.

Therefore $k\pi.(2R_{\phi''}.d + d^2) = 2\pi r^2(\sin \phi'' - \sin \phi')$ .... (i)

But $\angle QOQ'\text{c} = \angle POP'\text{c} = \dfrac{2\pi r.\cos \phi''}{R_{\phi''}} = 2\pi k$ .... (ii)

and, by applying the properties of similar sectors (OPP' and OQQ')

$$\frac{R_{\phi''} + d}{R_{\phi''}} = \frac{2\pi r.\cos \phi'}{2\pi r.\cos \phi''} = \frac{\cos \phi'}{\cos \phi''} \qquad \dots\dots\dots\dots\dots\dots\dots(iii)$$

Now, from these three equations it is possible to determine the values of k, $R_{\phi''}$ and d for selected values of ϕ' and ϕ''.

Thus, $k = \dfrac{\cos^2\phi' - \cos^2\phi''}{2(\sin\phi'' - \sin\phi')} = \tfrac{1}{2}(\sin\phi'' + \sin\phi')$ ...... (iv)

$$R_{\phi''} = \frac{2r.\cos\phi''.(\sin\phi'' - \sin\phi')}{(\cos^2\phi' - \cos^2\phi'')} = \frac{2r.\cos\phi''}{(\sin\phi'' + \sin\phi')} \quad \dots (v)$$

$$d = 2r.\frac{(\sin\phi'' - \sin\phi')}{(\cos\phi' + \cos\phi'')} \quad \dots\dots\dots\dots\dots\dots\dots\dots\dots (vi)$$

The calculations necessary to complete the projection can now be made as follows. Let R_{90} be the projected radius of the pole, and let R_{ϕ} be the projected radius of some selected parallel ϕ. Then the area on the projection between the parallel ϕ'' and the pole is $k\pi(R_{\phi''}^2 - R_{90}^2)$; but the area of this same zone on the globe is $2\pi r^2(1 - \sin\phi'')$.

Therefore $k\pi(R_{\phi''}^2 - R_{90}^2) = 2\pi r^2(1 - \sin\phi'')$, whence R_{90} can be determined; that is, the arc which is the projection of the pole can now be drawn.

The area on the projection between the 'apex' (O in *Fig. 25*) and the projected pole, which is an arc of radius R_{90}, is $k\pi R_{90}^2$. The area on the projection between the pole and the parallel ϕ is accordingly $k\pi(R_{\phi}^2 - R_{90}^2)$; on the globe the area of this same zone is $2\pi r^2(1 - \sin\phi)$.

Therefore $k\pi(R_{\phi}^2 - R_{90}^2) = 2\pi r^2(1 - \sin\phi)$, whence R_{ϕ} can be determined for any selected value of ϕ; that is, the arc which is the projection of any selected parallel of latitude can now be drawn.

The projection of a complete hemisphere is shown in *Fig. 65*, in which the two standard parallels are in latitudes 30°N. and 60°N. The two parallels are not *standard* in the sense used earlier in

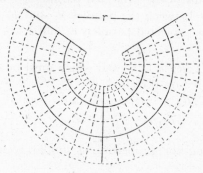

FIG. 65

CONICAL EQUAL-AREA PROJECTION WITH TWO STANDARD PARALLELS

The standard parallels are in latitudes 30° N. and 60° N. Meridians and parallels at intervals of 15°.

connexion with conical projection; they are not described with a radius $r.\cot\phi$; but they are of the correct length, namely, $2\pi r.\cos\phi$.

The following table gives the values of R_ϕ for selected values of ϕ, and also an indication of the comparative meridian scales, on the projection and on the globe.

$\phi°$	R_ϕ	Difference (projection)	Difference (globe)
90	0·379		
		0·114	0·262
75	0·493		
		0·239	0·262
60	0·732		
		0·268	0·262
45	1·000		
		0·268	0·262
30	1·268		
		0·253	0·262
15	1·521		
		0·231	0·262
0	1·752		

Thus, between the standard parallels, the meridian scale is too large; elsewhere it is too small.

On the projection, the length of the parallel ϕ is $k.2\pi R_\phi$; on the globe the length of this same parallel is $2\pi r.\cos\phi$. Thus, when $r=1$, it is only necessary to compare $k.R_\phi$ and $\cos\phi$, as in the following table:

$\phi°$	$k.R_\phi$	$\cos\phi$	$\phi°$	$k.R_\phi$	$\cos\phi$
90	0·259	0·000	30	0·866	0·866
75	0·337	0·259	15	1·039	0·966
60	0·500	0·500	0	1·197	1·000
45	0·683	0·707			

It will be seen that the scale along the standard parallels is correct; between the standard parallels the scale along the parallels is too small; outside the standards it is too large.

Summary of Properties. The *equal-area* property is preserved over the entire projection. The scale along two selected parallels is true; hence by a careful choice of 'standards', the scale along the parallels can be made reasonably accurate over a larger area than is possible with the *one-standard equal-area conic.* Between the standards the scale along the parallels is actually too small; here the meridian scale is too large. Outside the standards the scale along the parallels is too large; here the meridian scale is too small. Shape is therefore distorted, for 'stretching' in one direction must be counteracted by 'compression' in another, if the projection is to be *equal-area.* In the case of a country such as Britain, which extends through only about 10° of latitude, an excellent map results, for the two standards can be selected with a view to securing a good distribution of accuracy. It must be remembered, however, that in this projection the emphasis is on *equal-area*.

Limitations. As in the case of all conicals, the limitations become very apparent when the area mapped has a great extent in latitude, for then it is not possible to secure a reasonable distribution of general accuracy over the entire projection, even by a careful choice of standard parallels. The *equal-area* property remains true, of course, but the linear scales cease to be accurate; and as 'stretching' in one direction is accompanied by 'compression' in another, shape becomes increasingly distorted.

Construction. Let $R_\phi{''}$ be the radius of the projected standard parallel ϕ'', which is in a higher latitude than the other selected standard (ϕ'); then $R_{\phi''} = \dfrac{2r.\cos \phi''}{\sin \phi'' + \sin \phi'}$. The parallel ϕ'' is thus projected as an arc of a circle of radius R_ϕ, described about O, the 'apex' of the developed cone. This projected arc subtends at O an angle of $k \times 360°$, where

$$k = \frac{\cos^2\phi' - \cos^2\phi''}{2(\sin \phi'' - \sin \phi')} = \tfrac{1}{2}(\sin \phi'' + \sin \phi').$$

All projected parallels are then described as concentric arcs, bounded by the extreme meridians drawn from O to the ends of the parallel ϕ''. The radius (R_{90}) of the arc which represents the pole is given by the relation $k\pi(R_{\phi''}^2 - R_{90}^2) = 2\pi r^2(1 - \sin \phi'')$; the radius (R_ϕ) of the projected arc which represents the parallel in latitude ϕ is given by the relation $k\pi(R_\phi^2 - R_{90}^2) = 2\pi r^2(1 - \sin \phi)$. The meridians radiate from the 'apex' O at uniform angular intervals; thus, if meridians are selected at true intervals of $\theta°$, they will be projected at intervals of $k \cdot \theta°$.

THE ONE-STANDARD ORTHOMORPHIC CONICAL PROJECTION

The parallels are projected as concentric arcs of circles, and the meridians as radii of those arcs. Every parallel therefore intersects every meridian at right angles, an essential condition of orthomorphism. Further, although the actual scale necessarily varies from one parallel to another, the distances between the parallels are so adjusted that, at every *point* over the entire projection, the scale along the meridian is equal to the scale along the parallel. Thus, shape is preserved at every point, for (*a*) the intersections of parallels with meridians are rectangular, as on the globe, and (*b*) the scale along the meridian at any specified point is equal to the scale along the parallel at that point, also as on the globe. The variation in the actual scale from one parallel of latitude to another is of no significance in the representation of the shape of areas which approximate to *points*; but it is of paramount importance in the representation of the shape of extensive areas, for the shape of large areas is not preserved.

Let ϕ' be the latitude of the *standard* parallel; and let k be the value of the constant of the cone. Then, if R_ϕ be the radius of the projected parallel ϕ, it can be shown that the projection will be orthomorphic if $R_\phi = c\left(\tan\dfrac{(90-\phi)}{2}\right)^k$, where c is a constant which depends only on the scale of the selected standard parallel; that is, c depends upon the particular value of ϕ', but when ϕ' has been evaluated, c remains constant for that projection. The length of the standard parallel ϕ' must be projected true to the scale of the 'generating' globe. The true length of the standard parallel ϕ' is $2\pi r.\cos\phi'$; the projected length of this same parallel is $2\pi kc\left(\tan\dfrac{(90-\phi')}{2}\right)^k$.

Thus, $2\pi kc\left(\tan\dfrac{(90-\phi')}{2}\right)^k = 2\pi r.\cos\phi'$

whence $c = \dfrac{r.\cos\phi'}{k\left(\tan\dfrac{(90-\phi')}{2}\right)k}$, an expression which can be evaluated, for the value of $k(=\sin\phi')$ is known. Hence the value of R_ϕ can be determined for any selected value of ϕ.

The projection can then be completed as in *Fig. 66*, in which

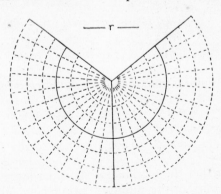

FIG. 66

CONICAL ORTHOMORPHIC PROJECTION WITH ONE STANDARD
PARALLEL

Standard parallel in latitude 45° N. Meridians and parallels at intervals
of 15°.

the standard parallel is in latitude 45°N., and in which the meridians and parallels have been drawn at intervals of 15°.

In the case illustrated ($\phi'=45°$), the value of k is 0·707, and the corresponding value of c is 1·865.

The length of the projected parallel ϕ (radius R_ϕ), which subtends an angle of $k \times 360°$ ($k.2\pi^c$) at the 'apex' of the developed cone, is $2\pi k.R_\phi$; the true length of the same parallel is $2\pi r.\cos\phi$. To compare the scale along the projected parallel ϕ with that of the globe, it is necessary to show the relation between $k.R_\phi$ and $r.\cos\phi$, as has been done in the following table for selected values of ϕ, when $r=1$:

$\phi°$	$k.R_\phi$	$\cos\phi$	$\phi°$	$k.R_\phi$	$\cos\phi$
0	1·319	1·000	60	0·520	0·500
15	1·094	0·966	75	0·312	0·259
30	0·894	0·866	90	0·000	0·000
45	0·707	0·707			

It will be noticed that the scale along the standard parallel is correct, but that elsewhere it is too great (except at the pole, which is correctly projected, as a point).

The amount of adjustment necessary to preserve the property of 'equal-stretching' at every point over the entire projection is given in the following table, which shows the distances of selected parallels from the standard parallel, both on the globe and on the projection.

Latitude°	0–45	15–45	30–45	45–60	45–75	45–90
Projection	0·865	0·547	0·265	0·265	0·555	1·000
Globe	0·785	0·524	0·262	0·262	0·524	0·785

By a process of subtraction, the following differences are obtained:

Latitude°	0–15	15–30	30–45	45–60	60–75	75–90
Projection	0·318	0·282	0·265	0·265	0·290	0·244
Globe	0·262	0·262	0·262	0·262	0·262	0·262

It is now clear that the meridian scale is too large, except in the immediate vicinity of the standard parallel; in other words, the inevitable exaggeration of the scale along the parallels is accompanied by appropriate exaggeration of the scale along the meridians. (Notice, then, how *orthomorphism* and *equal-area* require radically different methods of adjustment.)

THE TWO-STANDARD ORTHOMORPHIC CONICAL PROJECTION

In this projection, two selected parallels of latitude are made 'standard'; that is, both are projected at their true lengths, but as concentric arcs of circles, which are spaced at such a distance that the orthomorphic property is preserved. As in all other cases of conical projection, a better distribution of general accuracy is obtained when two parallels are made standard than when only one standard is employed. The *orthomorphic* property is not affected, of course, by the substitution of two standards for one; and, so far as purely *orthomorphic* considerations are concerned, there is little to be gained by the refinement, for a conical projection based on one standard parallel can be made strictly *orthomorphic*. The advantage is seen, however, in the representation of 'subsidiary' properties, such as linear scale and area, which are projected more accurately when two standards are employed than when the entire projection is dependent upon one only. That considerations of linear scale and area are of a subsidiary character in the present case, presupposes *orthomorphism* as the primary purpose for which the projection is required.

Let ϕ' and ϕ'' be the two standard parallels which must, therefore, be projected at their true lengths, namely, $2\pi r.\cos \phi'$ and $2\pi r.\cos \phi''$, respectively. They cannot both be projected as '*standard*' in the sense used earlier in connexion with conical projection, for that would imply that their radii were $r.\cot \phi'$ and $r.\cot \phi''$ respectively; but this is not the case. The resulting projection, however, has all the appearance of a developed cone, the constant of which may be regarded as k.

The two 'standard' parallels will thus bear a true ratio to one another when

$$\frac{2\pi kc\left(\tan \dfrac{(90-\phi')}{2}\right)^k}{2\pi kc\left(\tan \dfrac{(90-\phi'')}{2}\right)^k} = \frac{2\pi r.\cos \phi'}{2\pi r.\cos \phi''}$$

whence
$$k = \frac{\log \cos \phi' - \log \cos \phi''}{\log \tan \dfrac{(90-\phi')}{2} - \log \tan \dfrac{(90-\phi'')}{2}}$$

With this value of k (a constant when the values of ϕ' and ϕ'' have been selected) it is now possible to determine the value of c from either of the following equations:

$$c = \dfrac{r.\cos \phi'}{k\left(\tan \dfrac{(90-\phi')}{2}\right)^k}, \quad \text{or} \quad c = \dfrac{r.\cos \phi''}{k\left(\tan \dfrac{(90-\phi'')}{2}\right)^k}.$$

These values of k and c may now be used to determine the radius (R_ϕ) of the projected parallel ϕ, for $R_\phi = c \left(\tan \dfrac{(90-\phi)}{2}\right)^k.$ All parallels are projected as concentric arcs of circles, and each parallel subtends at the 'apex' of the developed cone an angle of $k \times 360°$. The two standard parallels are projected true to the scale of the 'generating' globe, and all other projected parallels are related to that scale.

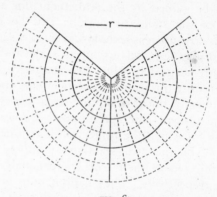

FIG. 67

CONICAL ORTHOMORPHIC PROJECTION WITH TWO
STANDARD PARALLELS
Standard parallels in latitudes 30° N. and 60° N.
Meridians and parallels at intervals of 15°.

The projection of a complete hemisphere is shown in *Fig. 67*, in which the 'standard' parallels are in latitudes 30°N. and 60°N., and in which meridians and parallels are shown at intervals of 15°.

The length of the projected parallel in latitude ϕ is $2\pi k.R_\phi$; the true length of this same parallel is $2\pi r.\cos \phi$. To compare the scale along the projected parallel ϕ with that of the globe, it is necessary to show the relation between $k.R_\phi$ and $r.\cos \phi$, as has been done in the following table for selected values of ϕ, when $r = 1$:

$\phi°$	$k.R_\phi$	$\cos \phi$	$\phi°$	$k.R_\phi$	$\cos \phi$
0	1·283	1·000	60	0·500	0·500
15	1·062	0·966	75	0·301	0·259
30	0·866	0·866	90	0·000	0·000
45	0·683	0·707			

The scale along both standard parallels is correct; between the two standards the scale along the parallels is too small; elsewhere it is too great.

The amount of adjustment necessary to preserve the property of 'equal-stretching' at every point over the entire projection is given in the following table, which shows the distances of selected parallels from the *nearest* standard parallel, both on the globe and on the projection:

Latitude°	0–30	15–30	30–45	45–60	60–75	60–90
Projection	0·583	0·273	0·255	0·256	0·279	0·699
Globe	0·524	0·262	0·262	0·262	0·262	0·524

By subtraction, where necessary, the following differences for a range of 15° are obtained:

Latitude°	0–15	15–30	30–45	45–60	60–75	75–90
Projection	0·310	0·273	0·255	0·256	0·279	0·420
Globe	0·262	0·262	0·262	0·262	0·262	0·262

Thus, *between* the two standard parallels, the meridian scale is too small; on the standard parallels, the meridian scale is correct; elsewhere it is too great. In other words, where the scale along the parallels is exaggerated, the meridian scale is exaggerated also; where the scale along the parallels is diminished, the meridian scale is diminished.

By a careful choice of standard parallels, it is possible to project an area, which has no very great extent in latitude, so that the scale is everywhere sensibly correct. Then it may be claimed that the shape of the area as a whole is preserved. In the case of areas which have a great extent in latitude, however, it is not possible to secure uniformity of scale; then the shape of the area as a whole is not preserved, and the limitations of *orthomorphism* immediately become apparent.

The projection of a country such as Britain, for example, is a simple matter compared with the projection of a continent such as North America. In the former case, a high degree of general accuracy, in addition to the one particular property required, is possible; in the second case, the degree of general accuracy achieved must necessarily be of a much lower order, although the one particular property required can be accurately projected.

CHAPTER VIII

CONVENTIONAL PROJECTIONS

AITOFF'S (EQUAL-AREA) PROJECTION

THIS useful projection may be regarded as derived from the *equatorial* case of the *zenithal equal-area projection* of a complete hemisphere (*Fig. 58*).

If the *zenithal equal-area projection* be 'projected' perpendicularly on to a *new* plane, which intersects the plane of the *original* projection along the equator, and which is inclined to the plane of the *original* projection at an angle of 60°, a '*new*' *equal-area* projection will result. The original bounding circle of *Fig. 58* will become an ellipse, the major axis of which (the equator) is twice the length of the minor axis (the central meridian). The area bounded by this ellipse is one-half the area of the original circle.

Consider now the transference from the original *zenithal*, to the 'new' projection, of the point of intersection of the meridian θ with the parallel ϕ. On the *zenithal*, let x be the distance of the point (ϕ, θ) from the central meridian, and let y be its distance from the equator. On the 'new' projection the position of this same point will be denoted by the co-ordinates x and $\frac{1}{2}y$, for distances measured in a direction parallel to the equator are not affected by the transference, whereas distances measured in a direction at right angles to the equator are reduced to one-half their original value.

A ready method of constructing an *equal-area* world map is thus available; but several modifications are necessary. The circular outline of the original *zenithal* represents a hemisphere; the elliptical outline of the 'new' projection must represent the complete globe. To make this possible, the meridian θ, when transferred to the 'new' projection, is numbered 2θ; the parallel ϕ remains the parallel ϕ. Thus the range in longitude of the original *zenithal* (90°E.–90°W.) is effectively doubled in the 'new' projection (180°E.–180°W.); the range in latitude is unaltered by the transference (90°N.–90°S.). The graticule of the 'new' projection has thus been adapted, merely by the device used in the renumbering of the meridians, for the world map (*Fig. 68*). Moreover, since the original *zenithal* was an *equal-area* projection, the 'new' projection must be *equal-area* also, for every unit of area

on the original *zenithal projection* is reduced to half a unit on the
'new' projection. The 'new' projection, however, is required to
represent twice the area represented by the original *zenithal*; thus,
if *r* is the radius of the 'generating' globe from which the original
zenithal was developed, the 'new' projection (*Aitoff's*), as constructed
here, may be regarded as developed from a globe of radius $\frac{1}{2}r$.

The great advantage of *Aitoff's Projection* is that the shape of
areas near the edges of the map is better than in *Mollweide's*

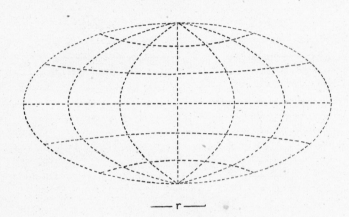

$$\longmapsto r \longmapsto$$

FIG. 68
AITOFF'S PROJECTION
Developed from the equatorial case of the *Zenithal Equal-Area Projection*.
Meridians at intervals of 60°; parallels at intervals of 30°.

Projection, for the parallels are curved and therefore intersect the
meridians less obliquely. Even so, the distortion is still great, as
is inevitable when the whole globe is projected on one map.

Projections such as *Aitoff's* and *Mollweide's* have little value
apart from the one purpose of showing the whole globe on one
map; but in this one respect they are invaluable. Both are
equal-area projections, an attribute of the highest order in distributional maps. Both, in an attempt to offset the gross distortion
which is inevitable in the projection of the whole globe, embody
a large measure of 'compromise'; but, as a result, properties,
which could be retained in the projection of smaller areas, are
sacrificed. For this reason, apart from the one property of *equal-
area*, these projections offer no particular advantage for maps
of individual continents. In short, they are best regarded as
essentially 'world-maps'.

RE-CENTRED PROJECTIONS OF THE WHOLE GLOBE

Sometimes, when it is desirable to preserve tolerably good *shape* over certain specified areas, together with *equal-area*, a *re-centred* projection can be used with advantage.

The general method will be at once apparent from *Fig. 69*, which is based on *Sanson-Flamsteed's Projection*, and from *Fig. 70*, which is based on *Mollweide's Projection*. In the northern hemisphere,

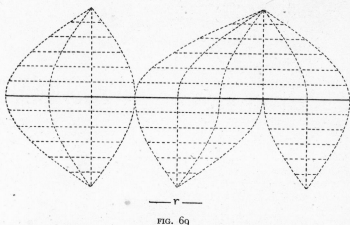

FIG. 69

SANSON-FLAMSTEED'S PROJECTION (RE-CENTRED)

Parallels at intervals of 15°; meridians at intervals of 45°.

both projections have been re-centred in longitudes 90°W. and 90°E.; in the southern hemisphere, they have been re-centred in longitudes 90°W., 0° and 135°E. These particular longitudes have been chosen merely to facilitate comparison with *Figs. 31 and 34*.

For a world map, concerned only with land masses, the projections could be re-centred in longitudes 100°W. and 80°E. in the northern hemisphere, and in longitudes 60°W., 20°E., and 135°E. in the southern hemisphere. Such an arrangement would give a fairly good representation of all the land masses, and the inevitable 'breaks' in the projection would occur mainly over the oceans, which, for the present purpose, are not a major consideration. The greatest distortion of shape would occur in Western Europe and Eastern Asia; but the land mass of Eurasia is so large that distortion cannot be avoided on a continuous map, whatever the method of projection employed.

If re-centred maps are required for the ocean basins, the 'breaks' in the projection should be planned to occur over the land masses.

Re-centred maps of this type have undoubted value when it is desired to make comparisons which involve *equal-area*, without undue sacrifice of *shape*, over the whole globe. Sometimes, however, the 'breaks' cause inconvenience, especially when a pronounced change of shape and longitudinal scale occur along what

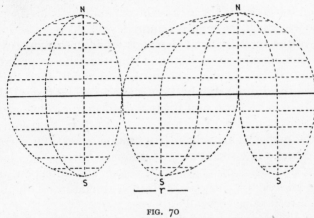

FIG. 70

MOLLWEIDE'S PROJECTION (RE-CENTRED)

Parallels at intervals of 15°; meridians at intervals of 45°.

is, in reality, the same line. Thus, in *Figs. 69 and 70*, in the northern hemisphere, the meridian 45° W., marking the *eastern* boundary of the western mass, and the meridian 45° W., marking the *western* boundary of the eastern mass, are really one and the same line; but the two projections of this one line are very different. In such circumstances, false impressions of 'fit' can easily be gained; but, provided no 'breaks' are allowed to interrupt the actual areas for which comparisons are required, incongruity is not conspicuous, while valuable compensation is manifest.

PART III

CHAPTER IX

THE CHOICE OF A PROJECTION FOR A SPECIFIC PURPOSE

THE choice of a suitable projection on any occasion depends, partly on the extent of the area involved, and partly on the precise purpose for which the map is required.

One of the most frequent demands made on a map is that it should show comparative distances and the relative positions of places accurately. If the area surveyed is small, such demands can be satisfied quite simply, for distances can be projected over the entire area at a constant fraction of their true values, and the intersections of meridians with parallels can be made rectangular, as on the globe. Then the representation is sensibly correct in every respect. The sheets of the Ordnance Survey, for example, fall into this class; distance, area, shape and direction are all sensibly perfect; the map is, in fact, a miniature of the actual area as if seen from vertically above.

When the area is large, however, the representation is less perfect, on account of the difficulties introduced by the spherical earth. In such circumstances it is necessary to select the one vital property, and to project it as faithfully as possible. The correct representation of one property will undoubtedly be accompanied by distortion in others, and it is therefore necessary to estimate beforehand how the best compromise can be achieved. Thus, in individual cases, the scale can be made correct (i) along all parallels and one or two meridians, (ii) along all meridians and one or two parallels; the scale cannot be made correct along all parallels *and* all meridians.

When one characteristic has been decided upon, others follow as an inevitable sequence. If, therefore, in an *equal-area* projection, the scale along the parallels is too great, the scale along the meridians must be too small; but if, in an *orthomorphic* projection, the scale along the parallels is too great, the scale along the meridians must also be too great.

In the following examples, certain basic requirements and guiding principles are examined.

World : Tropical Zone. For a map showing the world distribution of such products as rubber, tropical hardwoods, rice, sugar-cane, etc., which are all essentially tropical or sub-tropical, distortion in high latitudes is of no significance. An *equal-area* world map, giving good representation in tropical and sub-tropical latitudes, is thus the first consideration. If the main purpose is comparative distribution, linear scale and shape, although desirable, are of secondary importance. The question of transport, however, is often bound up with that of distribution; so distance may become a very important, if secondary, consideration. Now, although the *equal-area* property can be achieved in a variety of ways, uniformity of scale is impossible on a world map; so also is the correct representation of shape. Of the *equal-area* projections already discussed, none could be ruled out as entirely unsatisfactory for the present purpose. Moreover, since all the products mentioned are confined to land masses, a re-centred projection could be used quite effectively. Of the continuous projections, *Aitoff's* is probably the best choice for a general map; but *Mollweide's* has achieved popularity, which has been well merited. Many would probably prefer *Lambert's Cylindrical*, for the rectangular intersections of meridians with parallels give a better impression of shape in low latitudes. Even *Sanson-Flamsteed's* could be used to show these particular regions with relatively little distortion of shape, for only about 280° of longitude are involved, and, by careful selection of the central meridian, the extreme edges of the map could be avoided. A further advantage of this projection is the correct representation of scale along the parallels. If the projection were re-centred, the representation of scale over the land masses could be greatly improved, for the obliquity of the extreme meridians could be reduced, thereby making the scale along all meridians more closely in agreement with that along the 'central' meridians, which are correctly represented. Such a projection would be a good compromise, embodying, *equal-area* with reasonable *shape* and good *distance*.

World : Temperate Zone. For a map showing the world distribution of such features as temperate forests, temperate grasslands, wheat-producing areas, etc., the problem is rather more complicated. An *equal-area* world map is again the first and essential consideration; but if it were the only consideration, any of the *equal-area* world maps already discussed would satisfy the requirements. In the generally higher latitudes which are now involved the representation of shape is difficult, and not very satisfactory on any of the projections. *Lambert's Cylindrical* would, however, probably be ruled out, for the longitudinal 'compression' necessary to balance the latitudinal 'extension' in high latitudes gives rise to marked deformation of shape. Deformation would also be pronounced in *Sanson-Flamsteed's*, for the edges of the map could not now be avoided; but if this projection were re-centred, many of the worst features of deformation could be greatly reduced. Of the continuous maps, *Aitoff's* would again be a probable choice; but popularity might well turn the balance in favour of *Mollweide's*. *Aitoff's* certainly preserves better shape than *Mollweide's* in the higher temperate latitudes, for the projected parallels are curved, and the intersections of meridians with parallels are accordingly less oblique. A re-centred *Mollweide's* can be used with good effect, for greatly improved shape in the regions that really matter can thereby be achieved.

Small Extent in Latitude. For a map featuring the trans-continental railways of Canada or Siberia, that is, a region which has a great east-west extent, but a relatively small north-south extent, very different considerations must predominate. It is necessary, for example, that the scale should be reasonably accurate over the entire area; and, as the two cases specified involve fairly high latitudes, some sort of conical projection is preferable. The *two-standard conic* would serve quite well for most purposes, for, by careful choice of the two 'standards', a reasonable degree of accuracy is possible over the entire region. If *area* happened to be a prime consideration, the *two-standard equal-area conic* might be preferred, while *Bonne's* has much to commend it. With each of these three projections it is possible to represent *area, distance,* and *shape* tolerably well; but *direction* usually needs careful interpretation, for the parallels are curved, and the meridians converge. For a zone with only a small extent in latitude, situated along, or near, the equator, *Sanson-Flamsteed's Projection* is generally a good choice, for the scale is correct along all parallels and the central meridian, and, within the limits of the area, not greatly distorted along the other meridians.

Small Extent in Longitude. For a map showing a great north-south route, for example, the 'Cape-to-Cairo Route', the chief consideration is the correct representation of a region which has a great extent in latitude, but only a small extent in longitude. *Sanson-Flamsteed's Projection*, with its central meridian carefully chosen so as to run through the middle of the 'strip', is generally a good choice, for, near the central meridian, *distance, shape,* and *direction* are all satisfactory, while *areas* are always strictly comparable. If, however, the region surveyed is confined to one hemisphere, for example, Adelaide to Darwin in Australia, a conical projection might be used with advantage. *Bonne's* would serve very well for most purposes, for the central meridian could be chosen so as to produce the minimum deformation. The *two-standard conic*, although serviceable for accurate representation of longitudinal distances, is not so satisfactory for distances measured along the parallels, when the map covers an appreciable extent of latitude. Admittedly, the stress in the question is on the north-south distance, but distances in an east-west direction are inevitable, and even small latitudinal distances suffer proportionate distortion. Such distortion may not be very pronounced on small-scale maps, but it may assume alarming significance on large-scale maps.

Small Regions. For a small region, such as the British Isles or France, the *two-standard conic* is eminently satisfactory for most general purposes, although modifications of it might be desirable under certain conditions. Thus, if *area* is to be the prime consideration, the *two-standard equal-area conic* would be preferable, but the differences between the two are not apparent on small-scale maps, and are generally less than the variations which might reasonably be expected to occur in the map sheet itself due to changes in atmospheric conditions. If *shape* is a predominant consideration, the *two-standard orthomorphic conic* would be preferable, although, on small-scale maps, the differences are again practically negligible. The *orthomorphic* projection, embodying, as it does, the principle of 'equal-stretching', also facilitates more accurate computation of direction; and in this respect it must be noted that the Ordnance Survey has made good use of a *Transverse Mercator's Projection*. For many purposes, *Bonne's Projection* makes an admirable map of a small area, for, by careful choice of the *central* meridian and *standard* parallel, the representation can be made sensibly correct in every detail; this projection has, in fact, been used as the basis of certain large-scale topographical maps of European countries.

Europe and Australia. For a general map of Europe, the *two-standard conic* is quite serviceable, since there are only about 40° of latitude involved; but if *area* is a prime consideration, either the *two-standard equal-area conic* or *Bonne's* should be used. The total extent in longitude is only about 60°, and, if the *central* meridian is placed in longitude 20° E., *Bonne's* does not occasion

any pronounced deformation of shape; moreover, *areas* are everywhere strictly comparable, while scale is sensibly uniform over
the whole of the region under consideration. Similar observations
might be made in the case of such regions as Australia and India.

Africa. For a map of Africa, *Sanson-Flamsteed's Projection* is
satisfactory for most general purposes. The greatest east-west
extent of the continent occurs in tropical latitudes, where the
projection is most accurate, and if the central meridian is placed
in about longitude 20°E., there is no pronounced deformation of
shape, for the intersections of meridians with parallels are roughly
rectangular. *Areas* are, of course, everywhere strictly comparable
and the linear scale is reasonably uniform, although, away from
the central meridian, the scale along the meridians becomes
somewhat exaggerated.

South America. Here, the considerations are broadly similar to
those which obtain in the case of Africa; if the central meridian
is placed in about longitude 60°W., *Sanson-Flamsteed's Projection*
can be used as the basis of a serviceable general map. There is
one important difference, however, namely, that the equator
crosses the northern part of the continent. In *Sanson-Flamsteed's
Projection*, the zone of greatest accuracy lies along the equator;
that is, across the northern part of the South American Continent.
Should it be desirable to bring the zone of greatest accuracy more
into the heart of the continent, a conical projection, such as
Bonne's, could be used with advantage.

Asia and North America. Large regions, such as Asia and North
America, which are situated mainly in temperate latitudes, present
many difficult problems, for it is quite impossible to avoid serious
deformation when they are projected on continuous maps. Both
continents are frequently mapped on *Bonne's Projection*, which at
least ensures equality of *area* in the representation. In the case
of Asia, the *central* meridian is placed in about longitude 90°E.,
and when the *standard* parallel is placed in about latitude 35°N.
there is a fair spread of accuracy. The zone of greatest general
accuracy then lies along the parallel 35°N., where the scale along
both meridians and parallels is true, and where the intersections of
meridians with parallels are rectangular. Away from this long
and narrow zone, the representation becomes distorted, except
along the central meridian; and in the 'corners' of the map, such
distortion is pronounced, due to the obliquity of the intersections
of the meridians with the parallels. For this reason, the *equal-area
zenithal (azimuthal) projection* is sometimes preferred; if the centre

of the projection is in about latitude 40°N. and longitude 90°E., there is nowhere the marked deformation which is such a disadvantage with *Bonne's*. In the case of the *zenithal projection*, however, the region of greatest general accuracy is around the centre of the projection; and away from this point, the representation becomes increasingly inaccurate, in concentric zones. There is thus a fundamental difference between the *zenithal equal-area projection* and *Bonne's*; the accuracy of the former is related to a point, whereas the accuracy of the latter is related to a line, in which case the distribution of general accuracy is greater. The precise purpose of the map may therefore determine which is the better projection in any given circumstances.

Polar Regions. The polar regions are best projected on some form of *polar zenithal*, the precise form depending upon the purpose of the map. Thus, the *polar equidistant* would ensure correct representation of distances measured from the pole; the *polar equal-area* would ensure that areas over the entire region were strictly comparable; on the *polar gnomonic*, great circles would be represented by straight lines; and on the *polar stereographic*, the shape of small areas would be preserved.

Direction. It has already been stressed that a straight line on *Mercator's Projection* is a line of constant bearing; and this property accounts for the use of the projection in navigation. At the same time it must be remembered that great circles provide the shortest routes over the surface of the globe. Great circles are not, in general, projected as straight lines on *Mercator's Projection*; but they invariably are on the *Gnomonic*.

APPENDIX I

ELEMENTARY PLANE TRIGONOMETRY

In the triangle ABC (*Fig. 71*), let $\angle BAC = \theta$, and let $\angle BCA = 90°$; then

$$\text{sine } \theta \quad (=\sin \theta) \quad = \frac{BC}{AB}$$

$$\text{cosine } \theta \quad (=\cos \theta) \quad = \frac{AC}{AB}$$

$$\text{tangent } \theta \quad (=\tan \theta) \quad = \frac{BC}{AC} = \frac{\sin \theta}{\cos \theta}$$

$$\text{cosecant } \theta \quad (=\text{cosec}\,\theta) \quad = \frac{AB}{BC} = \frac{1}{\sin \theta}$$

$$\text{secant } \theta \quad (=\sec \theta) \quad = \frac{AB}{AC} = \frac{1}{\cos \theta}$$

$$\text{cotangent } \theta \quad (=\cot \theta) \quad = \frac{AC}{BC} = \frac{1}{\tan \theta}$$

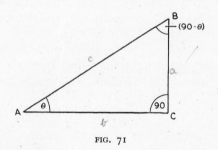

FIG. 71

$$\sin^2 \theta + \cos \theta^2 = 1$$
$$\sec^2 \theta = 1 + \tan^2\theta; \ \text{cosec}^2\theta = 1 + \cot^2\theta$$
$$\sin \theta = \cos (90 - \theta); \ \cos \theta = \sin (90 - \theta)$$
$$\tan \theta = \cot (90 - \theta)$$
$$\sin 2\theta = 2 \sin \theta . \cos \theta$$
$$\cos 2\theta = \cos^2\theta - \sin^2\theta = 1 - 2 \sin^2\theta = 2 \cos^2\theta - 1$$
$$\tan 2\theta = \frac{2 \tan \theta}{1 - \tan^2\theta}$$

The expression $\sin^{-1}a$ means 'the angle whose sine is a'; thus, if $\sin A = a$, then $\sin^{-1}a = A$.

APPENDIX II

CIRCULAR MEASURE

In *Fig. 72*, let *PQ* be a circular arc of radius *r* described about the point *O* as centre, and let θ^c be the circular measure of the $\angle POQ$; then

$$\frac{\text{length of arc } PQ}{\text{radius } r} = \theta^c, \text{ where } \theta^e \text{ is expressed in radians}$$

But $\dfrac{\text{circumference of circle}}{\text{radius}} = \dfrac{2\pi r}{r} = 2\pi$

therefore 2π radians $= 360°$

or   1 radian $= 57\frac{1}{2}°$ (nearly).

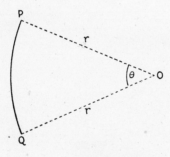

FIG. 72

APPENDIX III

AREAS OF ZONES ON THE GLOBE

In *Fig. 73*, which represents a section through the centre of a globe, parallel to the axis of an enveloping cylinder, which touches the globe along the equator *AB*, let *P* be a point in

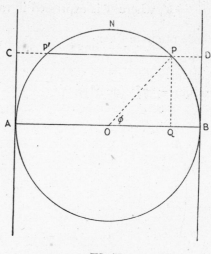

FIG. 73

latitude ϕ, and let *CPD* be a plane parallel to the plane of the equator. Then the area of the zone *AP'PB* on the globe is equal to the area of the cylinder intercepted between the planes *AB* and *CD*, namely, the belt represented by *CABD*. Thus, if the radius of the globe be *r*,

$$area\ AP'PB = area\ CABD = 2\pi r \times BD$$
$$= 2\pi r \times PQ$$
$$= 2\pi r \times r.\sin \phi$$
$$= 2\pi r^2 \sin \phi$$

But the *area* of the hemisphere is $2\pi r^2$.

Therefore the *area* of the zone *PNP'* is $2\pi r^2(1 - \sin \phi)$.

APPENDIX IV

THE ELLIPSE

In Fig. 74, let P be a point, the co-ordinates of which, when referred to the axes $A'OA$ and $B'OB$, are x and y; that is, $PN=x$, and $PM=y$. Let $OA=OA'=a$, and let $OB=OB'=b$. If, now, P moves in one plane so that its position with reference to the axes $A'OA$ and $B'OB$ is always given by the equation $\dfrac{x^2}{a^2}+\dfrac{y^2}{b^2}=1$, then the locus of P will be the ellipse $AB'A'B$.

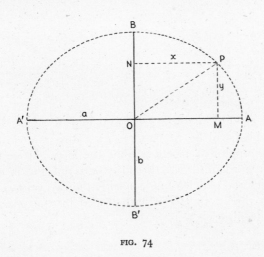

FIG. 74

Given the lengths of the axes, namely, $2a$ and $2b$, it is therefore possible to plot the ellipse, for the value of y, corresponding to selected values of x, can be determined by substitution in the above equation.

In *Fig. 75* the two foci of the ellipse are shown, namely, F_1 and F_2. It is one of the properties of the ellipse that, no matter where the position of P might be on the ellipse, the sum of the distances of P from the two foci is constant, and equal to $2a$. Let P be at B; then $F_1B=F_2B=a$; and $OB=b$. Then $(F_1O)^2=(F_1B)^2-(OB)^2=a^2-b^2$. Given the axes, it is therefore possible to determine the distance between the two foci, namely, $2\sqrt{a^2-b^2}$.

A simple practical method of constructing any required ellipse is thus available. Determine the positions of the two foci, F_1 and F_2; insert one pin at F_1, another at F_2, and a third at one extremity of the minor axis (B in *Fig. 75*). Draw a length of

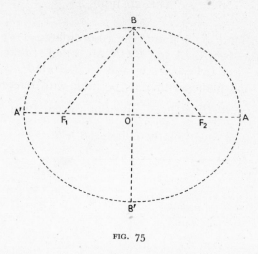

FIG. 75

thread taut around all three pins, and join in a closed loop, the length of which will be $2a + 2\sqrt{a^2 - b^2}$. Now remove the pin B, and place the point of a pencil inside the loop. Move the pencil carefully outwards until the thread is taut and flat on the paper. Finally, move the pencil round, outside the two pins, and always keeping the thread taut; the path traced by the pencil will be the required ellipse.

QUESTIONS

The sources of questions are acknowledged thus:

University of Cambridge	C
University of London	L
Joint Matriculation Board (Universities of Manchester, Liverpool, Leeds, Sheffield, and Birmingham)	N
Oxford and Cambridge Schools Examination Board	O & C

B.A. Honours and B.Sc. Special Examinations	(D)
Diploma in Geography	(G)
Intermediate Arts, Pharmacy, and Science Examinations	(I)
Higher School Certificate	(H)

1. Why is it more necessary to know the properties of map projections when studying small-scale atlas than large-scale topographical maps? **O & C (H)**

2. What benefits do a sailor and an airman derive from a knowledge of map projections? **O & C (H)**

3. With reference to the principles of construction and uses of four contrasted map nets show why different map projections are necessary. **N (H)**

4. Describe three of the chief types of map projection, and state what type of projection you would choose for a map of the Arctic regions, giving reasons for your choice. **C (H)**

5. What are the principal equal-area projections commonly found in atlases? Describe briefly the general principles of the construction of any one of them and note the chief uses for which it would be (a) desirable, (b) undesirable. **L (H)**

6. Name two projections that are used for maps of the world and discuss, with illustrative diagrams, the chief merits and defects of each. **L (I)**

7. The following is the list of projections and nets given in the syllabus for this examination: polar zenithal (gnomonic, equidistant, equal area), conic equidistant with one standard parallel, equatorial orthographic, cylindrical equal area, Mercator, Bonne, Sanson-Flamsteed, Mollweide. For each of four from the above list name an area, other than the world as a whole, for a map of which the projection could be used advantageously. Give brief reasons for your choice and indicate the features and the relations of the area which could be shown with advantage by the use of this projection. **N (H)**

8. Describe the main features, properties, and appropriate uses of each of the following projections: (a) polar zenithal gnomonic; (b) Bonne; (c) Mercator; (d) Mollweide. Select two of these projections and show how the graticule is constructed. N (H)

9. Describe the chief distortion effects produced by drawing a map of the world on (a) a Mercator, and (b) a Mollweide network, and hence show the chief kinds of purpose for which each is (a) appropriate, and (b) inappropriate. L (H)

10. In what respects does the graticule of (a) the Mercator, (b) the Sanson-Flamsteed (Sinusoidal) projection differ from that of the globe? For each of these projections, show for what geographical purposes the graticule renders it unsuitable. L (H)

11. What is the nature of the map projection known as Mercator's Projection? Compare this with any two other methods, and discuss their relative advantages and disadvantages. C (H)

12. How would you distinguish between the following pairs of projections: a Bonne's and a Simple Conic of India; a Sanson-Flamsteed and a Mollweide of Africa; a Polar Equal Area and a Polar Equidistant of Antarctica? O & C (H)

13. For each of the following maps choose the projection which is best suited: (a) ocean currents in the Atlantic Ocean; (b) the climatic regions of Africa; (c) Arctic pack ice; (d) mean annual rainfall in the Argentine Republic? In each case show why the selected projection is most suitable. N (H)

14. What projections would you use for maps to represent: (a) distribution of population density in India; (b) ocean currents in the Atlantic; and (c) a trans-polar air map? Justify your choice in each case. O & C (H)

15. For what purposes are the following map projections most suitable: Bonne, Mercator, Sanson-Flamsteed, Gnomonic? State briefly your reasons, and give the chief properties of each of these projections. N (H)

16. What projections would you use for: (a) an air navigation map of Western Europe; (b) a population distribution map of the same region; (c) an atlas map of Africa for general purposes? Justify your selections by describing briefly the properties of the projections which you recommend. C (H)

17. What projections are in common use for making Physical maps of England and Wales? Discuss their relative advantages. Suggest, giving full reasons, a projection suitable for making a Political map of the same area. C (H)

18. Explain how you would determine (a) the shortest route, and (b) the bearings to be followed, for a flight from Archangel to the Bering Strait. How would you estimate the distance covered? O & C (H)

19. It is proposed to prepare atlas maps to a uniform size (10 in. by 8 in.) of the following: (a) prevailing winds over the North Atlantic ocean; (b) relief and drainage in the Isle of Wight; (c) distribution of wheat in Australia. What projection and scale would you propose for each? What contour interval would you use for (b)? What unit dot would you use for (c)? Briefly justify your choice.　　L (G)

20. Give a concise account of the properties and uses of the Zenithal projections, and sketch the net of parallels and meridians for any one of the group.　　L (D)

21. Compare and contrast the properties and appropriate uses of Conical and Cylindrical Projections.　　L (D)

22. Select a projection which you consider suitable for the following, and give reasons for your choice: (a) to show a true bearing from one point to another; (b) to illustrate the relative size of different parts of the British Empire; (c) to compare the areas of land in the Arctic and Antarctic.　　L (D)

23. Describe an equal-area map net suitable for an atlas map of (a) Asia, (b) South America, (c) the world. Illustrate carefully the method of construction of one of the nets you select.　　L (D)

24. Explain the principles on which Mercator's Projection is constructed and sketch a portion of the net from 0°-60°N. and 0°-60°E. Show that a straight line represents a line of constant bearing; and indicate how the scale can be determined at a given point.　　L (D)

25. A straight line cuts the meridians on the Mercator projection and on the cylindrical equal-area projection at a constant angle. Explain why in the one case the straight line is useful to mariners, and in the other it is not.　　L (D)

26. For what maps would you use Bonne's projection? State the advantages and disadvantages of this projection.　　L (D)

27. Explain the principles underlying the sinusoidal projection, and show how you would construct a sinusoidal net to scale.　　L (D)

28. Explain, with suitable illustrations, the mode of construction and the properties of the Sinusoidal Projection. Indicate its relation to the Cylindrical and Conical Projections, respectively.　　L (D)

29. Discuss the essential differences between the Zenithal equidistant and Sinusoidal projections with regard to comparatively narrow areas running approximately equidistant north and south of the equator. Extend your remarks to the choice between these projections for an airways route map from Egypt to the Cape.　　L (D)

30. Describe three examples of projections exhibiting the property of orthomorphism. Which, if any, could you use to show a continent in its correct shape?　　L (D)

PRINTED BY
JARROLD AND SONS LTD.
NORWICH